Peenemünde
to Canaveral

PEENEMÜNDE
TO CANAVERAL

DIETER K. HUZEL

with an introduction by WERNHER VON BRAUN

PRENTICE-HALL, INC.

ENGLEWOOD CLIFFS, N.J.

TO IRMEL

THE WAY IT WAS

Twenty years ago, the first V-2 rocket—or A-4 as we Peenemünde men called it—was launched. From these humble beginnings, rocket engineering has advanced to the threshold of space exploration. A good deal has happened in the intervening time, to the world and, more specifically, to the rocket. Ideas not even close to the drawing board then are now old hat or well along toward realization. The large guided rocket which first came to life on the Baltic island of Peenemünde before and during World War II now occupies a sizable portion of Man's thinking: As a weapon, as a tool for the exploration of cosmic space, as a vast new challenge to many branches of engineering and science.

Twenty years is a long time in the fast moving Age of Space. Peenemünde has become a legend; the A-4 a touchstone, a kind of intellectual prototype. But Peenemünde was a *place,* and the rocket was its *product*—and where there are places and products there must be men. There was no magical waving of a scientific wand to create the A-4 rocket. It was the result of men working, working hard and with devotion to an idea which far transcended its imminent application as a weapon of war.

That is what this book is about—the men who made the large rocket a reality. It is told by one of those men, Dieter Huzel, who worked in all phases of the effort—in the field, on the test stand, in administration. He saw Peenemünde at the height of its historic place, and he saw it crumble under the effects of war.

Much has been written about Peenemünde, but mostly by peo-

7

ple writing from second- and third-hand information. Too much of this has been utter nonsense. It is time that a word was said about Peenemünde as it looked from the inside. And said by somebody in a position to know—somebody who was there.

Quite probably, I might differ with some of the views and evaluations in the pages that follow. But then, maybe I would have been looking at things from a somewhat different viewpoint. And viewpoint is the very key to understanding human relations. But this I do know: The man who writes about Peenemünde here tells a first-hand story, and the only axe he has to grind is that of the truth.

And I think there is a great underlying truth, a lesson for all of us today in the story of Peenemünde's rise and fall. Our contemporary newspapers are full of stories of missile and space rocket tests, of great successes side by side with heartbreaking disappointments. To the average citizen who hears how much depends upon the successful outcome of a particular launching, it must seem that with all this money and time—how can we still have "failures"? What most people do not realize is that in rocket engineering there is no such thing as a complete failure, that data is data—and each bit of data makes the next step more certain of success; that every new advance in technology, everything we accomplish in science and engineering is only the sum total of human effort. A rocket never learns what is wrong with it. It is the *men* who learn, the men who are building it. It was the men who made the A-4, and it is the men who are carrying on the job today.

So the proper story of Peenemünde is the story of its people; and in their struggle for success is mirrored the struggle of today's rocket men, in this country and, it may be presumed, in the Soviet Union as well. That, I believe, is the most important thing this book has to say.

What you read about Peenemünde in the following pages you may regard as the eye-witness account of a man who was there, for this is surely the most complete portrayal of life at Peenemünde that I have yet seen. The place is here: The streets, the buildings, the test stands, the sound of the waves breaking on the beach and of a mighty rocket engine filling the air with its window-rattling roar. The people are here: Struggling to keep equipment operating in the face of explosions, misfirings and air raids; trying desperately to accomplish their job in the face of ever-mounting odds, achieving ever-increasing success even as the means of achievement slipped from their grasp.

A man would have to have been there to recognize the accuracy of the picture presented here. And, of course, I was. These pages have brought Peenemünde vividly back to life for me.

This is the way it was.

WERNHER VON BRAUN

Huntsville, Alabama
November, 1961

CONTENTS

chapter

Peenemünde
to Canaveral

1

THE ROAD TO PEENEMÜNDE

"Launch switch to launch!"

"Key is on launch."

"Launch start!"

The final commands of the countdown had the staccato precision of rifle fire. Launch controller Albert Zeiler stared fixedly through the large window which provided an unobstructed view of the tall RS-1. With the closing of the "launch" key, a timer relay started ticking away. The liquid oxygen vent valve closed, and the little white vapor plume that had been floating gently from the frost-covered side of the missile was snuffed out.

The dozen or so people in the launch control center hardly breathed. Propellant tank pressurization would take 30 seconds. No one showed any emotion—only tension and apprehension. All eyes that could be spared from the launch control consoles peered with Zeiler's through the thick double-mirrored window at the silent bird without.

Several hours earlier, the first light of dawn had gradually lifted the silhouette of the 65-foot high rocket from the harsh embrace of the floodlights. Moments before the myriad of workmen attending to the bird's many pre-launch needs had scurried for cover as the wail of sirens and the blink of flashing red lights warned of the final moments of countdown.

Inside the half-buried concrete-reinforced blockhouse now all was silence, save for the steady click-click-click of the relay, the hum of electronics, final terse reports of pressure values building up in the rocket's propellant tanks, and occasional anxious but reassuring remarks of a guidance engineer intently scanning the array of dials and signal lights before him. Those 30 seconds seemed like an eternity.

"Tanks pressurized!"

A small bright flame burst from the tail of the missile.

"Pre-stage!"

The wiggling flame grew, billowed and engulfed the launching pad. Zeiler's sharp command was almost drowned out as the missile's roar slammed its way into the blockhouse. The noise rose to a deafening crescendo.

"Main stage!"

Flames and gases were ejected from the rocket at incredible speeds. Huge clouds of smoke and dust rolled up and were tossed about as if by a huge angry fist in their midst.

"Lift off!"

Slowly, unperturbed—serene, as it were, at Armageddon—the great missile lifted rock-steady and true. Sharp shock diamonds appeared in the white-hot flame of its exhaust as the missile rose clear of the turmoil on the pad.

Although it took no more than a few seconds, the missile seemed to remain in view in the narrow window a long time. But soon only the fiery exhaust still glared against the clear morning sky. Then it, too, vanished. Gradually the thunder of its powerful engine faded away. In the quiet that ensued, Dr. Kurt Debus, Firing Chief of the U.S. Army's Ballistic Missile Agency, turned from the window and remarked dryly:

"That's gone."

"That" was Redstone number one, the first large U.S.-built rocket ever to be launched. The place was Cape Canaveral, Florida; the time, 9:35 a.m., August 20, 1953. Debus' brief remark broke the spell in the blockhouse. Awed silence burst into a pandemonium of congratulations, dinning telephones, PA announcements and futile appeals for silence as the "count up" of telemetered reports of the missile's flight progress continued.

Hours later I lay stretched on the sands of Indialantic Beach.

Only here with the gentle pounding of the waves in the background, and the still-warm but pleasant late afternoon breeze blowing away any effects of the humid, mosquito-infested day's and night's work at the Cape, did I feel the full impact of what this day meant to me personally—even beyond its ultimate significance to America.

In an hour I would be joining the others of the launch team in a gay celebration of the event, but now my mind drifted back to the early days of 1946 and my arrival in America fresh from Germany and the group at Peenemünde which had developed the dread V-2. When we evacuated Peenemünde, the then-secret but now famous German Rocket Development Center on the Baltic Sea, many of us had given up all hope of ever again being able to work in the field of rocketry. Then and now, to most of us this meant "space travel"—the greatest challenge of the 20th Century—the embarkation to new worlds, exploration more bold in spirit and on a grander scale than anything since the days of Columbus.

But here we were in business again. The similarity to Peenemünde in many respects was almost beyond belief. The sands and reeds of Cape Canaveral could have been transported bodily from the Baltic coast. As before, Wernher von Braun was technical overlord, and there were Zeiler, Debus, Stuhlinger, and many others whom I had known and worked with for so many years. And, even though I myself worked for the foremost U.S. company in the liquid rocket engine field, Rocketdyne—or North American Aviation Aerophysics as it was then called—rather than with the old team at Huntsville, Alabama, I had nevertheless contributed my share to the success of this day.

I felt then that there must have been some kind of directed destiny to it all. Perhaps now I am convinced of it, for it was the Redstone that years after put America's first satellite into orbit and later boosted this country's first astronaut, Commander Alan Shepard, into space.

I rolled over and let the fine sand run through my fingers. How long it had been since I had done this on the Baltic beaches. What an unexpected course of events had brought me at 40 almost exactly to where, as a boy, I had dreamed I wanted to be!

Wars and their epilogues, it seems, have played a major role in my life. I was born in the industrial city of Essen in the Central Ruhr district of Germany just two years prior to the outbreak of World War I. Here, my father worked in the big Krupp factory, originally as a patent engineer but ultimately as head of the company's cinematography department. Though movies were still very much a novelty in those days, the Krupp management saw them—particularly those in slow motion—as an important aid in the study of ballistic phenomena. My father quickly immersed himself in this new field.

My first reliable memories are of ersatz food, blackouts, searchlights, anti-aircraft fire, and of endless columns of weary soldiers making their way back from the western front after the armistice. I remember, too, that while the street lights gradually began to glow again, the ersatz stayed with us for a long time. Lack of jobs, lack of food, and worthless paper money brought uprisings, shootings and demonstrations which kept the Ruhr in turmoil for many years.

By 1923, though things had quieted somewhat, the French Army moved in for occupation, which lasted more than two years. The high school in which I had just started was requisitioned as a barracks for the French troops, and we had to double up with another school.

Meanwhile, the Krupp factory, under stipulations of the armistice, was forbidden to manufacture arms. Departments which did not lend themselves readily to production of commercial items were simply dissolved. For my father this might have been a crisis, but he turned the attention of his cinema department—for perhaps the first time in any industry—to a new field: Technical training, safety, educational and advertising films.

To me, the most important result of all this was that my interest in engineering was whetted at an early age. Every so often my father would bring home fascinating bits of discarded film strips. I would splice these together and spend hours projecting them over and over again, until I knew every movement of every object by heart. Sometimes my father brought home complete rolls of technical movies which I projected with much excitement and studied with great interest.

Another factor in those early days conspired to point me in the direction of the sands of Cape Canaveral. This was an age of widespread German interest in rocketry. The names of many of the serious experimenters of those days are now part of rocket history—men like Max Valier, Hermann Oberth, Walter Thiel, Claus Riedel, and many others. As model airplanes captured the enthusiasm of American youngsters in the 1930's, so rockets were a source of endless excitement, and an even more challenging toy, for German children of the 1920's. My friends and I were among those who built and tested many model rocket devices— toys which foreshadowed the rocket craft that have so absorbed my adult life.

One of my most vivid memories from those years is of a lecture on rockets and space travel delivered by rocket pioneer Max Valier. On October 28, 1928, he spoke in an auditorium in my home town of Essen, and during the intermission I approached him, accompanied by one of my rocket-building chums. Proudly, we showed him some short movie strips my father had made of our model rocket car.

Our enthusiasm was shattered when, to our chagrin, Valier did not appear at all interested in the pictures. Instead, he delivered an on-the-spot stinging lecture on the dangers of rockets in young boys' hands. He concluded with a stern admonition that we stop such "tests" immediately. By a strange fate, Valier himself died less than two years later while experimenting with liquid propellant rockets, thus becoming one of the first to give his life to this new field of endeavor.

Despite such minor setbacks to my enthusiasm, I am convinced that the events of those years contributed materially to my growing desire to become an engineer. The coming of radio, the development of the automobile, the arrival of so many of our modern technological marvels—these things intensified that desire. Thus, after graduating from high school I enrolled in the Technical University at Stuttgart, whence I was graduated as an electrical engineer, and almost immediately joined the firm of Siemens-Schuckert in Berlin.

Oddly enough, at this point, when I finally became a practicing engineer, events combined to prevent me from pursuing my interest in rocketry. Shortly after Hitler came to power in 1933, news of rocket experimentation became increasingly rare and finally disappeared altogether from the German public press. We know now that, with the approval of the Minister of National Defense, the Ballistics and Munitions Branch of the Army Weapons Department had taken over virtually complete control of further German rocket development and decreed that it be conducted in complete secrecy. For the Treaty of Versailles, which so meticulously listed all of the weapons of war that Germany could not produce, failed completely to mention rockets.

The rocket and astronautical societies tried to keep alive the idea of the rocket ship and space travel, but because of the restrictions which prevailed they did not succeed. As a result, the people simply lost contact with rocket progress—which is just what the authorities wanted. Rocket development continued, however, under then-Major Dr. Walter Dornberger, first at Station Kummersdorf West, 17 miles south of Berlin and later (starting in 1936) at Peenemünde.

Meanwhile, I was engrossed in my work at Siemens where, except for occasional random reflections, I thought little about rocketry. I was still at Siemens as a project engineer in 1939 when World War II began. During the first war years, occasional, tantalizing rumors would reach some of us employed in large engineering companies—strange tales of a fantastic facility on the Baltic Sea where top secret weapons were being developed. But the powers that were in the Third Reich kept the lid on so well that I learned the real secret of the facility only by accident.

It was on a warm, moonlit summer evening in 1941, shortly before the German armies invaded Russia, that the dream of rocketry and space travel again burned its way into my consciousness. Though I certainly did not realize it at the time, this was the first in a fateful series of events that ultimately was to land me right in the middle of my childhood toys grown into full-size reality.

World War II had been raging for almost two years. Most of Continental Europe—except for Sweden, Switzerland, Spain, and Portugal—was under Axis control. The Luftwaffe was trying to pummel Britain into submission, and the first bombs had long since begun to fall on Germany.

I was with an old friend, Hartmut Kuechen, waiting at a bus station in blacked-out Berlin, after a day of sailing on the nearby Wannsee. I was full of talk about Irmel, a pretty, dark-haired girl from Siemens who had been with us.

As is so typical in this day and age of the working woman, Irmel and I had met, at first, strictly at the business level. For almost a year our relationship had been confined to the exchange of typewritten documents about transformer specifications, switch details, power stations. I do not remember what I had first noticed: her flattering ability to read my handwriting, her attractive feminine, girlish appearance, or her pleasant way of talking.

We lived in different parts of the city, and the chances of running into one another outside the office were about as remote as they are today in Los Angeles or New York. Yet a benevolent providence, which has made up the minds of millions of self-styled bachelors before, pushed me into the same subway compartment with her one day, when on my way to visit a friend. Since it was obviously silly to talk about transformers and order forms, we soon discovered that we both liked boating, dancing, the same books. More important, we found out that we were both free the next weekend.

My sailboat on the Wannsee, her "collapsible" on Tegel Lake, it really didn't matter. It was always fun, even if we did get caught in a thunderstorm occasionally. There usually followed a romantic evening walk from the moorings through pine forests to the city railway station (not always the nearest one). We'd be holding hands—or more likely, as it is more customary in Germany, interlocking arms—and would stop once in a while for a tender kiss. The war was now in its second year, and the future was uncertain. Thus, we enjoyed the present. We did not talk about the future, but I think we both felt that if we should survive the war, we would still be together.

Hartmut listened indulgently like an older brother. He was in the city on business from his job at a huge factory under construction near Stettin, northeast of Berlin. Although I had always assumed that this factory was part of a gasoline cracking plant near there, I had sometimes regarded his carefully guarded explanations of his work as somewhat suspicious.

Our conversation turned to the magnificent full moon and the soft glow of its light. We could not enjoy its beauty without being aware of the danger it presented as it made the blacked-out city a perfect target for Britain's night bombers. Suddenly, Hartmut turned to me and said:

"Dieter, maybe the day when man will visit our shiny satellite is closer than most people think."

My mind, working subconsciously, immediately sensed the full impact of his apparently casual remark. All of the experiments and excitement of my youth, when the idea of space travel had seemed but a step away from our tiny rockets, came rushing back to mind. I blurted out:

"So that's what you're building up north!"

He froze. I remember staring at the shocked expression the moonlight revealed on his face. The moment passed quickly, but I had so shattered his guard that he could only nod, and then change the subject.

After that, any hint in the newspapers about super-secret weapons brought that scene, so brief and yet so revealing, to mind. And I would wonder, a bit longingly perhaps, but never dreamed then that I could ever become part of such a project. Shortly, fate and the war intervened. In December 1941 America officially entered the war against the Axis—forced to act by Japan's devastating assault on Pearl Harbor. In the winter of 1942 the German steamroller assault across Russia was stopped, stymied, and hurled back at Stalingrad. The dreaded two-front war was on in earnest; the German Army in the East was in retreat and needed more soldiers. In March, 1942, I was drafted.

The story of my days as a soldier is, I expect, similar to the story of all soldiers: discomforts, frustrations, endless marching, a complete lack of any sensible objective from one moment to the next, the general misery of war. As a further frustration, my duties on the Russian front made no use whatsoever of my degree and years of experience in engineering. I was a *Landser,* an ordinary foot soldier, and my real capabilities, along with those of thousands of other good technical people drafted in a similar manner, were lost to the now-desperate German war effort.

But there is a universal lesson in those experiences; one which perhaps has even greater relevance today than then. Since I was both by inclination and training an engineer and was steeped naturally in the culture of my native Germany—a nation outstanding in its engineering achievement—I had no concept of what the Prussian military mind could be like. It is a mild statement to say that my exposure to it was shocking and disillusioning as I realized more and more how inefficient and inadequate the rigid, traditional military frame of reference could be when concerned with matters outside its own particular sphere. This view was later confirmed in my experiences with developmental engineering operations which had been placed under military control.

My life on the eastern front was one of chaos, confusion, exhausting, futile marches, jolting boxcars, and just generally wasted effort. Not only had we not been trained as hard fighting troops, but no one seemed to have figured out just how to integrate thousands of scientists and engineers into the ground army. Fortunately, by now it was late spring, and in the beginning, at least, we were not afflicted by the bitter Russian winter that had contributed so much to the German defeat at Stalingrad. But there was mud, oceans of mud, and dust, depending on the weather of the moment. Long marches with heavy packs to no apparent logical destination for no apparent reason did little to improve our morale and make us feel that we were really contributing something useful. Everywhere people seemed to be so busy being an army that there was little effort left to devote to doing what an army is supposed to do. But army life is army life.

After an uncomfortable rail trip across Lithuania that took much longer than it need have, we entered Russia on June 2. When we arrived at Vitebsk the following noon, we began to see signs of war—the first many of us had ever seen, because for the most part, Allied bombing of Germany was still light, sporadic, more of a sleep robber than a city razer. Smolensk was a scene of utter destruction. Only the rail yard, just recently rebuilt, seemed to be operative. All about were immense and shocking heaps of scrap metal—thousands of tons of Russian and German material. What an eloquent testimonial to the voracious appetite of war, I thought bitterly as I peered out the open boxcar door. It was a thought which would not leave me, for the farther we advanced into Russia, the worse the devastation became. Later, Germany was to look as bad, but I do not believe the possibility of a German defeat entered any of our minds then—despite the serious situation in Russia and the fact that American might was beginning to pour into the fray in ever mounting volume. We were, I suspect, too much taken with our own personal moment-to-moment problems. For weeks we were ordered to travel by foot, truck, and rail from one place to the next and as often as not back again.

Finally, I was transferred to the Zentral Ersatzteil Lager, a spare parts depot of the Army Group Center at the village of Kostjukowka outside of Homel. Reason: I could print well by hand!

At the depot, all of the various German automobile and motorcycle manufacturers maintained parts and supplies. Each division in the Central Army maintained a small group of representatives there, of whom Technical Sergeant Moesta, who had come up with me, and I were typical. Our job was to process parts requests sent in by our division; fill the orders, pack them, and arrange for delivery. For administrative purposes all of the divisional representatives were gathered into a company—which resulted in a very loose, practically independent organization.

I will never forget the appalling insight this assignment gave me into the sad state of German military logistics—particularly with regard to transport. There were at least 20 automobile and motorcycle manufacturers represented, and, sure enough, each division had vehicles of each make, though sometimes no more than one. This Gordian knot was compounded by the fact that each manufacturer had a surprising number of models. It was necessary to know the serial numbers of the chassis, the engine, and the body, plus a great deal of additional descriptive detail in order to obtain a correct part for a given vehicle. Complete parts stocks were nonexistent, and we had a tremendous log of back orders. Scores upon scores of vehicles were immobilized throughout the Central Army—and, by inference, throughout the entire

German Army—simply because a part or two was not available.

It seemed clear to me at the time—and my opinion with the advantage of the intervening years of retrospect remains unchanged —that this ill-considered complexity was a primary contributor to Germany's defeat in Russia. In contrast to the myriad of vehicle makes and models in our own forces, the Russians had only three major truck models: the Russian Ford, the Zis, and the Stalin. To be sure, they were crude by Western standards, having no elaborate features, built with wide tolerances, and guilty of high gas consumption. But, they worked, withstood the Russian winters, and had the immense advantage of interchangeable parts.

German equipment was not designed to meet the extreme Russian environmental conditions. This is not to say that the German General Staff did not take Russian weather into consideration. It was simply that nature just did not abide by the specifications. Winter was early the year of the invasion. The campaign was scheduled to be over before the first snowfall, and there was no planning for the alternative case. There is a lesson for today in this:

It is a misconception that any war can be waged on a single, given basis; that no back-up is required; that one branch of the armed forces, one weapon type, or even one pushbutton can assure victory.

In a few weeks I was on the move again. The entire depot was relocated to Kursk, far to the east and close behind the front lines. My Russian tour now took me from Homel to Brjansk, then to Orel, and finally to Kursk. The depot was being readied at nearby Ryschkowo when I arrived.

By now it was late fall and the onslaught of winter brought subzero temperatures in early November. I always think of that winter when it is cold. Russia and coldness are closely associated in my mind even to this day.

Just before Christmas a certain Sergeant Emil Kessler arrived to take over as my immediate supervisor. Kessler was the next link in the chain of events that was to take me into V-2 development. At the time, however, this was farthest from my mind. I was only a private assigned to a spare parts depot in Russia in the dead of winter!

Kessler was a man who had made a science of getting along in the army. As long as he was around, regular army food was only a supplement. His methods ranged from clever salesmanship (applied alike to Supply Sergeants and the wives of Russian farmers) to some activities which in civilian life are defined in the penal code. Fatefully, his personal procurement activities required a considerable number of trips, some of which he thoughtfully assigned to me. My big break came shortly after Kessler returned from a "business trip" he had arranged for himself to his home town in Germany. The "business" was for me to accompany a boxcar full of old truck tires to Warsaw to be exchanged for new ones. From there I was to proceed to Frankfurt am Main to pick up heavy duck for truck roofs. Although there was little hope of getting the duck, Frankfurt was Kessler's home town and I would be able to deliver a carton of eggs to his wife. It also gave me a chance to get back to Germany.

As expected, there was no duck. I delivered the eggs and was then able to visit my parents in nearby Essen. I was horrified to discover that heavy bombing had nearly pulverized this beautiful city. My parents, fortunately, were unharmed.

In working my way back to the eastern front, I managed a stopover in Berlin, where I still maintained a small apartment. My purpose was to visit Irmel, who was by now my fiancée. Indeed it might well have been my last opportunity to see her, the way things were going on the eastern front. Those few days of her warmth and petite beauty helped restore my faith that one day again the world might be at peace and that she and I might find a future together. Time passed quickly. Berlin had not been so badly bombed that the metropolitan life of theaters, cozy restaurants, and beautiful parks could not still be enjoyed.

Of significant importance to me was the arrival in town of my old friend Hartmut Kuechen. I made it a point to visit him. He told me that the government had finally felt the loss of the many technical and scientific people it had drafted into the rank-and-file army. A number of engineers-become-soldiers had recently been transferred to the secret facility on the Baltic coast where Hartmut worked. My mind flashed back to his chance comment months before about travel to our "shiny satellite." I immediately expressed interest.

"I rather thought you would," he said. "I will see what I can do for you. But," he added, smiling, "it may take a while. It's a military installation."

I returned to the Russian front with some hope of an improvement in my status. But, somehow I wasn't very confident. I reflected on this sadly belated appreciation of wasted manpower. In the spring of 1943, the German government realized that the outcome of the war was—to say the least—in doubt, and turned almost in desperation to the "miracle" weapons which were then given the very highest priority. But the resources of skilled labor and professional engineers at home were severely depleted. This forced the army to turn to its own ranks—to the technicians, engineers, and scientists who had become Landsers. An unwritten military law is that nobody drafted shall ever be involved in anything he has learned as a civilian. That law was now breached.

Overnight, Ph.D.'s were liberated from KP duty, masters of science were recalled from orderly service, mathematicians were hauled out of bakeries, and precision mechanics ceased to be truck drivers.

Then, at last, a letter from Hartmut confirmed our conversation. Soon after, July 13, 1943, my orders came through. Instantly my outlook on life changed. It was a dream come true. Even as it is with most rocket engineers today, the fact that I would be primarily developing a weapon did not enter my mind. There were—and are—things bigger than this. To me, the notification of transfer was more than a simple order. It was the start of a career, and the opportunity to participate in the birth of one of the greatest ages of all time.

I looked at the transfer order again. It read:

"Peenemünde."

On the evening of July 29, 1943, three weeks after the Allies had successfully invaded Sicily as the first step in the long and arduous Italian campaign, Hartmut Kuechen met me at the railway station in Koserow, a small hamlet and vacation spot on the island of Usedom, at the northern tip of which is Peenemünde.

There were friendly greetings, the pleasure of again renewing an old friendship, and grateful thanks for the change in my fortune which Hartmut had helped arrange. He immediately invited me to stay at his house for a couple of days. That evening he would say little about his work, despite my repeated probing.

When I awoke the next morning, the sun was high in the sky. I rose reluctantly. Hartmut's landlady had set up a bed for me on the glass-enclosed porch—with mattress, sheets, and a pillow, things I hadn't enjoyed in months. I hated to leave them. But kitchen noises brought the realization that I was hungry. As I shaved I could see, through the open window, a small fenced yard below with a couple of dozen chickens running around busily. Beyond were fruit trees and, partly obscured, other buildings. The deep blue sky was studded with white clouds: *Ein Wetterchen zum Eierlegen,* "a little weather fit to lay eggs." I repeated the common saying without thinking how much or little sense it made. For the first time in months I felt good.

Hartmut had left hours earlier to catch the train for the plant, and only the landlady was left. A simple breakfast was waiting: simple, that is, only by her standards. There were fresh rolls, an egg, and fresh milk—things which, like the bed, I hadn't known for a long while. I chatted with her as I ate and soon learned all about her children and grandchildren and their activities and mishaps.

"Well," I announced as I finished my cup of *Ersatzkaffee,* "I think I'll go down to the beach and look around a little. Which way?"

She gave me a few simple directions, but warned:

"Don't be late for lunch. One o'clock sharp."

Outside the house I breathed the clean fresh air exultantly. It carried the smell of the sea, of pine trees, and of ripening wheat. I followed a trail through pines and beeches. Then, abruptly, the woods ceased on the brink of an almost vertical cliff. Perhaps 150 feet below ran a wide strip of sand, blinding white in the midmorning sun, and hemmed by the gently thrashing surf whose murmur blended with the rustling of the trees at my back.

From my vantage point, the sea appeared almost smooth. The wind, cloud shadows, and the varying depth of the water mottled its surface with faint patterns of blue and green. In the distance the horizon merged imperceptibly with the sky. A few fishing boats dotted the water, their muffled *put-put-put* rising and fading with the wind. Such a first sight of the sea had always filled me with excitement. Today the impression was more intense than ever—in unbelievable contrast to the boredom and futility of the months just passed.

Hartmut had given me a road map of northern Germany, which I now took out. Berlin showed at the lower rim, with roads radiating out in all directions. There was the blue ribbon of the Oder River, fifty miles east of the capital, winding almost due north to the Baltic Sea. I smoothed the fluttering map against the wind and spotted the point where the Oder forms a huge delta on the Baltic, with the industrial city of Stettin at the southern tip.

I looked closely at the map. The delta does not open directly to the sea. Instead, it is almost completely blocked by two massive islands, Wollin on the east and Usedom on the west. Only three narrow passages to the sea exist.

This was my first trip to Usedom, but the map showed I had not been far away when I had visited the island of Rügen some years before. I looked up to see if it was visible from where I stood, but there was only the almost perfectly straight line of beach fading into the haze. Names so familiar to me dotted the Usedom shore: Swinemünde, Heringsdorf, Zinnowitz, as well as smaller settlements such as Koserow.

But where was Peenemünde? It took me a while to locate it— near the northwestern tip of Usedom—on the coast facing the mainland, at one of the three arms of the Oder. Peenemünde: "The mouth of the Peene River." Indeed, there is such a river, little more than a creek, winding across the mainland into the westernmost arm of the Oder.

Suddenly I noticed a stairway to my left leading down to the beach. Minutes and 200 steps later I was walking in the clean, grinding sand. In a *Strandkorb*—roofed wicker settee—I put on a pair of trunks borrowed from Hartmut and proceeded to enjoy thoroughly my first ocean swim at Peenemünde.

I spent the afternoon exploring Koserow, which I found to be a sleepy little village. I finally wound up at the railroad station some time before Hartmut's train was due. As I waited, I relaxed and watched the typical small-town activity. The train rolled in from the north and disgorged about a hundred people. I soon found Hartmut looking tired but cheerful.

"Another one of those days," he grumbled. "Don't ever go near that place!" He smiled. "How've you been?"

I recounted the day's events.

"All rested now, eh? Full of pep, energy and ideals? All right, you asked for it! Tomorrow I deliver you to the plant."

Next morning we boarded the train to the development center itself, about 25 miles north of Koserow. The train was made up of old cars, which had been abandoned by the German Federal Railroad around 1930 and clearly had been called back into service solely for war use.

"Top man at the plant," Hartmut began, as the train pulled out of Koserow station, "is Dr. Wernher von Braun, a tremendously effective individual and the guiding force behind the whole operation. Young, too; 32, I think." He scowled. "Unfortunately, his influence is limited to technical matters. You see, we also have quite a bit of brass around. With few exceptions, though, their chief concerns seem to be saluting and the officers' club. Otherwise they just get in our way."

He sounded bitter, and I remarked on it. I thought I had left all this far behind on the eastern front.

"This is not private industry, remember," Hartmut reminded me, shaking his head, and then adding, "You also will have to forget some of the engineering procedures manual you may still be carrying in your head from the old days at Siemens. It's not really bad here, but it's certainly different."

The train was moving at fair speed now, and the trees which had shrouded the tracks on both sides from the time we left Koserow were thinning. Pastures came into view and occasionally a grazing cow. To the right, a road gradually emerged and finally paralleled the tracks. Beyond, a dike blocked the view of the sea. Soon, the train ground to a stop.

"Where are we?" I inquired.

"This is Damerow. There used to be a village here, but it was washed away in a storm about a hundred years ago. Now, it's

only a checking point, the first of several we have to go through."
He pointed out of the window. "Here is the dead-end arm of the
Peene River. It almost touches the tracks."

A guard, about 50 years old and wearing a nondescript uniform, proceeded from bench to bench. Hartmut presented his identification tag, and I, my travel orders. The guard grumbled an
"Okay," and went on. Soon we were on our way again.

There was another brief stop at the village of Zempin, and then
the train finally chugged into Zinnowitz: a one-time fashionable
beach resort now occupied almost exclusively by Peenemünde
people. Hartmut rose and I followed him out of the train. We
passed through the gates into the hall of a typical small-town
railroad station. There was considerable activity; I noticed many
Army and Air Force uniforms.

"We're nearing the plant now. You should see the station
around 6:30 or 7:00 in the morning when the trains from Swinemünde and Wolgast are arriving one after another, and passengers are changing over to electrics. It reminds you of the Berlin
U and S stations at rush hour."

It was a short walk from the Federal Station to the Plant Terminal, a plain wooden structure, low and with a flat roof. Inside,
there were no ticket windows. Various announcements were posted
on the walls: Time tables; *What You See, What You Hear, When
You Leave, Leave It Here;* a simple: *To The Trains.*

Of several gates only a couple were open at this time of day.
We presented our papers to men in Army uniforms and passed
through on to a long platform, flanked by tracks. On our left,
near the building, was a huge bicycle rack, filled. We were alone
on the platform. Then I saw the waiting train and exclaimed:

"Why, this is the Berlin *S-Bahn!*"

There it was, the familiar modern design of the *S-Bahn* car—
large windows, stylish interiors, automatic double doors. We
walked along the platform. We entered a door near the middle
of the train and found seats by a window.

A whistle sounded. The train started and picked up speed
rapidly. The brief clattering over switches and crossovers soon
smoothed as we found the single track leading from the Zinnowitz yard to the south entrance of the plant. As an experienced

S-Bahn rider, I had been following the sounds of the motors operating in series and now found myself waiting for the second group
of steps with the motors in parallel, somewhat like waiting for
the other shoe to drop in the apartment above. But there was no
other shoe.

"Why doesn't he go faster?" I exclaimed.

Hartmut chuckled.

"That's rather embarrassing. Somebody slipped up. The voltage
of the rectifier stations doesn't match the train motors. And there
aren't any priorities or funds available to correct it now."

The train moved steadily onward, the humming of the motors
accompanied by the regular *clink-clink, clink-clink* of the wheels.
Presently pine trees closed in on both sides. A crossroad, secured
by closed gates, came into sight and slipped by. The sound of a
signal bell faded in, suddenly changed pitch, and faded out again.

"This is Trassenheide," Hartmut said as we passed through a
small village. "Only a few trains stop here. Once there were plans
to build a city here with a population of 30,000 or so. After
the war, maybe. . . ." He knocked on the wooden bench—an
automatic, unconscious action. "Now, there is only a large construction camp—mostly laborers from the captured eastern areas."
He paused and peered out. "You'll see the camp in a second. It's
a small barracks town, typical standard structures. However, you'll
find most of the buildings around here rather pleasant—a little
bit Third Reich maybe, but not obtrusively so. Certainly nothing like the colossal Nuremberg buildings or the monstrosities in
Berlin with their columns." He nodded. "Here's the camp now."

To our right, a chain-link fence seven or eight feet high swept
into sight. Behind it the barracks were dark, dull structures lined
up at fixed intervals. The trees began to thin on the other side of
the track. A highway paralleled the railroad, the only access road
to the plant. Typical farm-style houses equipped with outhouses
appeared. The train ground to a halt at a narrow, black-topped
platform marked Karlshagen. The village itself was obscured by
trees. Almost immediately the train began to move again. Hartmut
rose:

"We'll be getting off in a minute."

We stepped to one of the doors, and I looked through the window. The forest suddenly disappeared, as if someone had drawn aside a curtain. The track doubled, branched out, redoubled. The train wheels raised an angry *clatter-de-clap-clap* over switches and crossings, and then subsided again like the cackle of a briefly aroused chicken.

Neat two-story dwellings lined the rail yard, and I could easily imagine being in the suburb of a large city. The roofs were steep, after the style taught and practiced in the city of Stuttgart, where the University had a renowned architectural faculty. It was a style of moderation: solid brick buildings, stuccoed over, two or occasionally three stories high, with side windows and shutters. They were painstakingly adapted to the environment, with a little borrowing from historic places like Rothenburg or Nuremberg. Roofed platforms closed in, and the train came to a stop. We were there.

The camp was comprised of a group of some twenty one-story buildings, arranged in the shape of a horseshoe, all with the narrow sides facing the one-way road, like cows at a water hole. We passed the guard at the gate and entered a building to our right. A noncommissioned officer briefly inspected my papers.

"Report to the Master Sergeant of the Fourth Company, *Haus Wuerttemberg,*" he snapped.

"That must be the masters of science building," surmised Hartmut as we walked down the sidewalk. "All these single story buildings are occupied by platoons of *Versuchs-Kommando Nord*" —Test Command North—"which is composed of several companies, staffed by a number of officers and under a Colonel. The unit was formed as a device for transferring experts out of regular army units, without actually separating them from the army." Hartmut laughed. "So, you are still in the army! However, you will find your military duties not too strenuous, just a nuisance."

Anyone overhearing this remark would have been somewhat surprised, for Hartmut himself was wearing the uniform of a Lieutenant. He had come to Peenemünde under circumstances somewhat similar to mine. Having served out his reserve training requirement long before the war, he finished this tour with the rank of lieutenant. He remained a member of the reserve. Later, when he joined Siemens, he was put in charge of an important construction project at Peenemünde. In 1941 he had been recalled by the army but was immediately transferred back to Peenemünde, this time in uniform. This change, which was certainly not essential to the performance of his work, imposed on him all the disadvantages of being drafted and, on top of this, deprived him of his good salary in exchange for the considerably lower lieutenant's allowance.

"All the buildings in this part of the camp are essentially large bunk rooms, occupied by uniformed mechanics and technicians —whose rank depends entirely on their circumstances when transfer caught up with them. Here, rank is completely unrelated to assignment. Imagine an engineer in a private's uniform directing a bunch of mechanics, some of whom are NCO's."

"Your MS degree," Hartmut continued, "gives you some privileges insofar as housing is concerned. Also, did I mention that you will be paid a salary like the civilian engineers? You will most likely start in Group III. The soldier mechanics are paid a wage too, with lots of overtime. Only we officers are stuck with our military pay."

We halted before the double doors of a painted grey-green building, and Hartmut broke off his flood of information.

"Here we are," he said. "You're on your own now. Take care of yourself. See you Sunday for a day on the beach."

I watched him as he made his way back toward the station. Then, suddenly excited, I turned and entered the building.

2

INSIDE PEENEMÜNDE

I found myself in a long hall with white walls. A large bulletin board announced that this was *Haus Württemberg*. At first the building appeared to be completely deserted. The noises and smells so typical of military barracks were completely absent. Then I heard the rustling of papers. Through a half open door to the right I saw a Sergeant seated at a desk. I checked my uniform, tugged my tunic smooth, marched in, snapped to attention, and announced smartly:

"Private First Class Huzel reporting for duty!"

The Sergeant started, looked up from a novel he was reading, smiled, and waved a casual "At ease."

"I am the Master Sergeant of the Fourth Company," he said, putting the book face down on his desk. "Let's see your papers."

I handed them over. He scanned them and said:

"I'll keep the transfer order and the pass book, for the proper entries. Now let's see . . ." He turned to a wall cabinet festooned with keys. "Here, take room 108, top floor. You'll share quarters with Soldier Dr. Wittig. See me later for bedding and towels."

He handed me a key. I picked up my bag and snapped to attention again. But the Sergeant had already returned to his novel. I shrugged and left.

In 108, my roommate was out. It was a fair-sized room, with one window opposite the door. This was flanked by two cots flush against either wall. In addition were a closet, table and desk lamp, and two chairs. A sink—cold water only—occupied one corner.

Hot water, I learned later, was available in the one bathroom on each floor of the building. Suddenly I felt weary. I dropped my bag, stretched out on the bare cot, and let the events of the last few days meander through my mind. I felt a soothing quiet. Only once in a while the clapping of boots on the cobblestones outside rumbled up, then quickly faded away. With my arms under my head, I watched the summer clouds drift slowly across the blue square of the window. I finally dozed off.

It was hunger, I guess, that finally woke me. The sun was high in the sky. I got up, shoved my bag under the bed, and made my way back to the Master Sergeant, who was still engrossed in his novel. I asked him what I must do to obtain food.

"You will have ration cards, just like the civilians," he replied. "With them you can buy tickets at the messhall over in the service building, or, if you like, you can buy lunch tickets at the plant messhalls, of which there are several. For dinner, you can eat at the service building or take the train to town. In Zinnowitz there are several good restaurants." He smiled. "We have no curfew, but be sure to have a pass if you leave Usedom Island."

He glanced at his watch.

"You won't get your ration cards until afternoon. I'll write you a slip for today. Incidentally, there is a small shop in the basement of the service building where you can buy sausage, butter, jam, biscuits, and the like . . . for ration coupons of course."

He filled out the slip with a bold scrawl.

"There. And here is your travel order back. Use it as a pass until I've gotten a permanent one for you. Apply to plant protection for a badge."

After a lunch of better than average messhall food, I headed, on foot, for the personnel department. Outside the camp gate, I turned right and followed the road north: first past the station where we had arrived that morning. Beyond it lay the *Siedlung*— housing project—half hidden by trees, shrubs, and vines. Laundry fluttered peacefully in the light breeze. I could hear children's voices, muffled but happy.

Next came the maintenance hangars for the plant's electric trains. A good 500 feet long with four parallel tracks, this might well have been part of Berlin's *S-Bahn* or the Hamburg elevated.

The road swung right past the main entrance to the housing project. The style was unmistakably Third Reich. A massive swastika glared from the middle of the architrave. Long rows of all-the-same houses framed the gate building.

Less than half a mile ahead I spotted a large isolated concrete structure. This was my goal, the new *Werk Süd*—Plant South—administration building. Despite its unfinished state, it was clearly occupied. Signs of construction were everywhere: equipment, piles of piping, bricks, sand, gravel. Temporary two-story structures stretched like fingers from the rear of the main building.

I entered. The noise of numerous typewriters filled the air. I asked for a Corporal Dohm, who proved to be another refreshing example of this "civilian" army. When I had identified myself, he turned to a pretty dark-haired girl busy at a typewriter.

"Miss Klinger, please hand me the file." She rose and placed a file box before him. "Now . . . you're an *electrical* engineer."

Well, I thought, this was a step forward!

"We have several requests. Mr. Bruetzel of BSM and Mr. Maas of BGS have been making the most noise. Try them first."

BSM was *Bord, Steuer und Messgeraete*—Flight, Guidance, and Telemetering Devices—and BGS was *Bau-Gruppe Schlempp,* an independent department responsible for the entire plant construction program. Dohm gave me directions and asked me to have Bruetzel and Maas call him regarding the outcome of the interviews. A Mr. Sundermeyer, he added smiling, would make the final decision.

No one seemed to be in any hurry to get me to work. No one asked for my carefully rehearsed explanations for the time spent in transit to Peenemünde. The civilian casualness of it all was difficult to get used to. The trying business of the constant alert, the automatic feeling of guilt at the mere sight of a trim uniform, the old frustration of motion for motion's sake were fast fading. I sighed with relief. Outside, the summer air was fresh and clean, the afternoon sun bright and warm, and the war a long, dim way off.

My next appointments were still farther north. I caught a train. We passed a number of industrial buildings, barely visible through the trees. No more of the forest had been cleared than absolutely

necessary. One enormous hangar, however, loomed above everything else, more than 250 yards long and nearly as wide. Later I
learned that it was *Fertigungshalle 1,* or simply F-1, Mass Production Plant No. 1. This was the first unit of *Werk Süd* put under
construction and was just about to go into operation.

I left the train at *Werk Nord*—Plant North—station and, asking my way here and there, walked through busy streets flanked
by office and laboratory buildings. In due course I arrived at the
Telemetering Building, BSM Section Headquarters.

In a large, comfortable office on the second floor I met Mr.
Bruetzel and his assistant, Mr. Gengelbach. We talked—interminably, it seemed—mostly about my professional background.
I became uneasy at their apparent reluctance to accept me immediately and assign me to a working group. I tried to reason
with myself that any newcomer must be evaluated, but this logic
didn't help much. Upon my departure from the interview, Mr.
Bruetzel was politely friendly but showed no real sign of interest in my capabilities. Apprehensively, I felt the cold threat of the
Russian front again.

Doubling back past the railroad station, I soon reached the
BGS district. It was a mixture of residential and office buildings.

From the outset, the atmosphere was entirely different. Mr.
Maas was a heavily built man, lively, and good humored. He discussed my background only briefly, and then declared that he
would take immediate steps to have me assigned to his office.

I responded with enthusiasm. It hardly registered that I might
not be working directly with rockets. In fact, later, I realized
that I really didn't have any idea at all of my future assignment.
At the time, however, everything seemed fine. I was about to
become a part of Peenemünde. The Russian front once again
receded into distant memory. Mr. Maas and I chatted a while
longer, and I left. Through sun-filled streets, then in the shade
of stately pines which were there long before there had been a
plant, I strolled to the station and caught the next train back to
the camp.

Several days passed uneventfully. One of them I spent on the
beach at Koserow. Otherwise I just waited. Impatience smoldered.
I could not understand why it should take so long to assign me.

I am convinced that man without mission is the most frustrated of creatures. Moreover, I had yet to see my first rocket. Then, one evening, Hartmut promised to show me around on the next day.

I had just finished shaving and was putting on my uniform jacket.

"Five minutes to go," Wittig said.

He was referring to the regular morning roll call, a superfluous carryover from regular military service. I had watched it a number of times from the window, but this was to be my first experience.

Soldier-masters of science and soldier-doctors fell into three ill-adjusted ranks in front of the building, straggling up sleepily, tightening belts, inserting buttons as they walked. The Master Sergeant strolled on the sidewalk, showing no particular concern. Shouts from the ranks urged him to hurry. "We'll be late for the train!" was mingled with jokes and remarks aimed at the latecomers. I wondered in amazement what would happen next. Bored, barely audible and tired, came the command: "Attention. Left face. Forward march."

That was all. A strange motley group it was. The only "weapons" these soldiers carried were brief cases, small books, a miscellany of packages. A few munched sandwiches. The company was a buzz of conversations. I tried to synchronize my step with the man in front; then with the man in back. It was impossible. I gave up in a flurry of apologies for what I was doing to the heels of the man ahead. From a strictly military point of view, this was a mess. Personally, it was a pleasure.

At the station there was no command to halt. The group simply disintegrated into the stream of civilians pouring from the village across the tracks. To this day, I haven't the slightest idea what happened to the Master Sergeant. Maybe he left us at the service building. At the time I wondered why they kept us in the army at all. I still do.

"Werk Nord!" The train lurched to a halt, and there was a great commotion and shoving to the doors. The cars emptied almost completely, only a few people remaining on the train for the journey to *Werk West,* a Luftwaffe installation at one time

closely linked to the rest of Peenemünde but now largely independent. This was the birthplace of *Kirschkern*—the Cherry Seed —later to be known as the V-1 buzz bomb. I followed the crowd toward *Haus 4* where I was to meet Hartmut.

3

SCIENCE FICTION
ECLIPSED

I strode, almost ran, up the wide steps, between the columns, and through one of the three doors that marked the main entrance to *Haus 4*. Inside was a small lobby, to the rear of which rose an impressive stairway. A guard emerged from a cubbyhole and asked to see my papers. I inquired as to Hartmut's whereabouts. He directed me to a room farther in the building.

It was crowded with furniture and painted a standard dull grey. Three cluttered drawing boards lined one wall. Behind them a number of people were busy at work. Subdued conversation was audible. Opposite were desks and tables stacked with drawings and catalogs. The walls were bare except for a calendar and a scattering of small pictures. I sat down and waited, and in due course Hartmut appeared.

"There is a bus going north," Hartmut said, "but first we'll walk a little, so I can point out the sights."

Against a brisk sea breeze we walked down the macadam paved plant roads. That walk stands out vividly in my memory. First we passed the Materials Research Laboratory, a two-story brick building. Across the street was the combustion chamber pickling plant. Next came the supersonic wind tunnel, then the largest in the world, and opposite it, the liquid oxygen production plant, its compressors growling with a deep throaty roar. The test stand support workshop—*IW Nord*—faced the Valve Laboratory and the Maintenance Workshop. We arrived at an intersection, and

I could see other buildings in the distance, the huge hangar of the Assembly Shop and the Component Shop. Still farther down the road was the now-familiar Telemetering Building.

Ten minutes more brought us into the propellant storage area, distinguished by several wooden buildings, countless fuel drums lined up in orderly array, a line of railroad tank cars, highway tankers, etc. Signs reading *Rauchen Verboten* warned us against smoking. From this point the road led into a dense forest. We halted.

"And now for the test area," Hartmut announced. My excitement must have showed, for he smiled. "It's a twenty-minute walk to Test Stand P-7. We'll ride."

He hailed a passing truck which took us down a long straight stretch of road through the woods. Then, as it began to curve gently to the right, Hartmut pointed:

"That's P-1—*Pruefstand 1*," he explained. "We'll start our tour there, and thence to P-7 which is our largest. There, ahead, you can see it through the trees."

P-1 was a large block of concrete surmounted by an elaborate steel superstructure used for static firings of the A-4—later called the V-2. Hartmut described the entire testing operation in detail.

It was a whole new world: The flame deflector of molybdenum-steel pipes cooled by high pressure water from a nearby pump house crouched down deep below the retaining structure; the concrete base, designed so that railroad tank cars loaded with propellant could be moved right inside the test structure and connected to the missile fill lines; the logical simplicity of the whole complex assembly. The massive foundation also housed the recorder room, a small shop, an office, compressed nitrogen storage cylinders, catch tanks, and a variety of auxiliary equipment. My excitement as we climbed about was matched only by my growing impatience to see a rocket, for P-1 was empty. I hurried Hartmut towards P-7.

P-7's big hangar loomed above the trees—perhaps 100 feet high, 150 feet wide and 185 feet long, large enough to house a good-sized blimp. But this was only one part of P-7 which, in reality, was an entire test area. Its heart was an elliptical enclosure surrounded by a high sloping earthen wall, not unlike an

American football stadium or a Roman amphitheater. At one focus of the ellipse was a large symmetrical flame deflector, installed in a wide concrete-lined ditch. In testing, a movable structure complete with missile was rolled out into the arena and positioned over the flame pit, where it was tanked, checked, and finally fired. Complete, matching connections for pneumatic supply, instrumentation, and power lines were provided at the flame pit.

During static firings, three huge pumps imbedded in the earthen wall drove water at a rate of thousands of gallons per minute through the cooling tubes of the flame deflector. This cooled the deflector internally and protected it against rocket exhaust temperatures of 4,500 degrees Fahrenheit and up.

Close to the deflector was a launching pad—nothing more than a concrete slab supporting a steel table-like structure and a cable mast. At the far end of the earthen wall was the control center, a massive concrete cubicle containing offices, workshop, recorder rooms, cable terminals, static firing and launch control equipment, and a row of periscopes for viewing the missile safely from within.

Outside the earthen enclosure were numerous auxiliary stations: cold calibration stands for checking out engines and components without "live" propellants, the powerhouse where generators and batteries supplied a wide variety of electrical voltages and frequencies, a transformer station, and a propellant storage area. All of these features I picked out as we approached and Hartmut described them. Now he led me into the vast hangar.

It took a moment for my eyes to adjust from the brilliant sunlight outside. But I could hear; it was a busy place. There was activity everywhere. The rumble of small vehicles and the whir of auxiliary electric motors was punctuated by the intermittent sharp hiss of compressed gas (nitrogen, I soon learned, being used to check out valves and other high pressure gas components). A voice kept shouting for repeated operation of a certain switch on a console. Two overhead cranes squeaked, hummed, and rumbled to the staccato fire of orders shouted abruptly, apprehensively: "Over here! Hold it! Easy now!" The clang of metal and a thousand noises I couldn't identify converged in a cacophony of busy, purposeful sound. From a row of windows high in the far wall, shafts of sunlight cut diagonally through the haze.

Gradually my eyes adjusted, and then I saw them—four, fantastic shapes but a few feet away, strange and towering above us in the subdued light. I could only think that they must be out of some science fiction film—*Frau im Mond,* "The Girl in the Moon" brought to earth.

I just stood and stared, my mouth hanging open for an exclamation that never emerged. Then, slowly, I walked around them. They fitted the classic concept of the space ship—smooth, torpedo-shaped—giving no hint of the complex mechanisms within, and resting tip-toe on the points of four swept cruciform fins. By today's standards the A-4 was a small missile, but these were 46 feet tall and by all odds bigger than anything I had ever dreamed of. They were painted a dull olive green, and this, said Hartmut, as well as their shape had won them the nickname of cucumber. I laughed, and the spell was broken.

I tore my eyes away and followed Hartmut to a row of large stalls set against the opposite wall. Here, more missiles were suspended for easy access from platforms placed at various heights. The boattails—the aft fuselage with the fins attached—had been removed from all of these missiles, and I could see the rocket engine clearly.

Hartmut did his best to explain that maze of tubes, pipes, valves, wires, and containers. His monologue spilled over with terms that were completely new to me, terms that today are familiar to every school child: liquid propellant, combustion chamber, nozzle, steam plant, decomposer, thrust, specific impulse, mass ratio, cutoff velocity. I am certain that I took back with me only a cursory understanding of the principles and mechanisms that were soon to become so familiar to me. But what I did take away was an assurance that I had seen as reality what before had existed only in my imagination.

"The A-4," Hartmut continued, "is a true ballistic missile. When the engine cuts off, which we call *Brennschluss,* guidance control as well as propulsion ceases. The rest of the way the missile coasts." We climbed up to one of the platforms beside a missile with the boattail detached and the engine fully exposed. "Our propellants are liquid oxygen and seventy-five per cent (150 proof) alcohol. They are supplied to the combustion chamber, here, by this turbopump. To operate the turbopump, we use steam generated by eighty per cent hydrogen peroxide, decomposed by a liquid potassium permanganate catalyst in the gas generator, here."

"Pumping rates must be pretty high," I ventured.

Hartmut nodded.

"About 1,100 gallons per minute for the alcohol; 1,000 gallons per minute for liquid oxygen."

"You mentioned a ballistic trajectory," I said as we descended again to the hangar floor. "Over what range?"

"Nominally, 200 miles. *Brennschluss* occurs 63 seconds after launch, about 18 miles up. At this point the missile is traveling about 3,300 miles an hour in a slant climb. It coasts up to a peak altitude of around 60 miles, at which time it has tilted over into a horizontal attitude and its speed has dropped to 2,600 miles an hour. On the way down, air resistance slows it to an impact velocity of 1,750 miles an hour. Impact occurs roughly 320 seconds after launch."

We climbed to the top level of the stalls, and I leaned against the railing to savor the excitement, soak in every detail, and to contemplate the meaning of what I saw. Across the way, a mobile test structure cradling a missile was being serviced. Apparently it had just been brought in, for the huge doors at the end of the hangar were still open. Outside, I could see the earthen dike and the upper portion of another test structure behind that. An empty *Meiller-Wagen* crawled through the middle of the hangar. I asked Hartmut about this strange vehicle. It was, he said, a specially designed road-going trailer for transporting the A-4 rocket, serving simultaneously as an erector and service platform during launch operations.

This *Meiller-Wagen* had just been relieved of its cargo, and the first step in preparing the missile for static test had begun.

"Die Hose runter!" shouted Hartmut over the din, as he pointed.

I laughed. "The stripping of the panties" was what he had said. This, he explained, was shop talk for boattail removal. Numerous "panties" lay on the floor or hung from a special rack running the length of the hangar.

"Come now," said Hartmut, touching my arm. "We'll have to hurry to get even a quick look at the rest of the test area."

Reluctantly I followed him back down to the hangar floor. As we stepped out into the sunlight a door closed behind us, and the noise of the cranes, the shouting, and hissing grew fainter and mingled with the subdued sounds coming from the nearby electronics laboratory and the machine shop.

We crossed a lawn on the way to the massive concrete P-7 control center set astride the earthen wall. Off to the side we passed a huge pile of coal, black and opulent against the summer green. I thought of those cold, cold winters in Berlin and Russia, where we would have given most of our pay for just a few buckets.

Inside the P-7 control center were a spacious office, conference room, a small dormitory with double bunks, an adjoining shower, and a wash room. We hurried quickly through, and once out in the arena, it was only a short walk to the edge of the flame pit.

The massive test structure I had seen from within the hangar had now been moved over the center of the pit. It held an A-4 firmly in its metallic grip. Line and instrumentation hookups for static firing were being completed, and propellant tanking was in progress on the far side. The missile whined, groaned and crackled —in complaint, as it were—as the deadly cold liquid oxygen poured into its structure. A white coating of hoarfrost crept up the fuselage as moisture in the air condensed and froze around the lower tank.

Hartmut and I rode an elevator up to the second platform where mechanics were busy checking and readying the missile's steam plant for firing. The test structure was ingenious. A gimballed support permitted swinging the entire missile in two planes up to five degrees from the vertical, for guidance and control tests during static firing. A German-made Toledo scale, on which a movie camera was focused, measured thrust by means of a 100-to-1 lever reduction system. Additional facilities included relay and distribution boxes, the firex system, instrumentation lines, and movable and removable working platforms. As we rode the elevator down, I remarked hopefully:

"Now all that's missing is to see an actual test."

"Well," remarked Hartmut, "we might just do that."

He disappeared through the rear door of the control center, and soon returned, smiling.

"We're in luck. They're through tanking, and the test should go off in just fifteen minutes. You can't get into the control room without special clearance, but the top of P-1 makes a nice box seat. We'll have to hurry though."

We left the arena through a tunnel adjacent to the control center, and trotted hurriedly back to P-1. There we climbed to a forty-foot-high platform, where we had an unobstructed panoramic view of P-7.

There was a breathless beauty to our surroundings. Nature contrasted dramatically with the man-made wonders before us. To the right washed the Baltic Sea, calm and sparkling in the warm July sun. Lazy waves caressed stretches of pearly white beach, and a thick belt of reeds far down the shoreline undulated gently. The breeze blew lightly across the Peene River toward the mainland. The dense woods of the island seemed to merge with those on the mainland, reaching far away to the western horizon. Here and there isolated objects protruded from the woodland sea —buildings of the Luftwaffe's *Werk West,* and the steeple of the cathedral in the little town of Wolgast on the mainland. As I watched, an airplane descended into the trees that hid the *Werk West* airfield from view.

Next to the earthen wall of P-7 and separated from it by a narrow belt of trees, a large graded area stretched toward the sea. It was empty except for a *Vidal-Wagen,* little brother of the *Meiller.* This was P-10, intended originally for development launchings.

Beyond P-10 lay the northen tip of Usedom, and beyond that, the sea. On clear days, Hartmut remarked, the little island of Oie, scene of much earlier A-5 tests, a small-scale development version of the A-4, could be seen. On such days even the white cliffs of the distant island of Rügen stood out.

I turned my attention to P-7, where occasional shouts and the whine of platform motors mingled with unintelligible fragments from the PA system. A number of people still moved about the test structure, but gradually, as if by some invisible force, they were being drawn away, disappearing into the control center. At first the retreat was casual, then more and more hurried, until finally the last man left at a run, waving an "all clear" to the man at the periscope.

Then suddenly P-7 was deserted, silent. Only a delicate swirling vapor cloud swinging gently from the end of one of the fins gave evidence that time had not simply stopped. Then seconds hung like minutes. Nothing stirred. Then a hawk soaring lazily over the trees caught my attention. Subconsciously, my eyes followed its graceful sweeping flight.

Suddenly the harsh sound of a siren slashed the silence, blared for a moment, and stopped.

"This is it," whispered Hartmut.

The vapor cloud receded and vanished. I heard the faint hissing of streaming compressed gas.

"Liquid oxygen tank prepressurization," Hartmut explained. The hissing stopped, started, and stopped again in regular cycles. A second later, a brilliant flame blossomed at the tail of the missile.

"Ignition!"

Hartmut had hardly spoken when a sharp double click sounded. Immediately a billowing orange flame burst from the tail of the missile, wriggling and pulsating like a living thing for a few seconds, until it steadied into a short, feathery vertical flame. I heard a low rumbling noise.

"That's pre-stage . . . now watch!"

Abruptly, the flame became bright yellow and shot violently straight down into the pit. A diamond pattern steadied into shape in the flame, stabilizing as if nailed there. Exhaust gases, mixed with water vapor from leaking cooling pipes, boiled and were thrown high out of the pit with sharp violence. Unbelievable noise tore at my ears and chest with physical violence. At first the roar was steady. Then it began to oscillate irregularly, and clouds of smoke and steam pulsed and rolled to the rear in time with the throbbing beat.

The noise was overpowering. The seconds—60 of them—dragged painfully, intolerably. Then rapidly the flame began to shrink. The shock diamond changed swiftly, and with a loud hollow howl, the flame disappeared. The shrill whistles of tank vents, purges, and water sprays became audible, and one after another died out. Almost immediately engineers and mechanics flooded into the arena and converged on the test structure. Platforms lifted into position, and securing operations were soon underway. The test was over. I turned to Hartmut.

"What an experience! The sound!"

It was always the noise that left the most unforgettable impression. Not just the loudness, which defies description. It slams at you with real physical violence, tears and twists at your insides. It can make you writhe in general over-all discomfort, even pain. And it is everywhere, inescapable. Only when you have heard a rocket engine fired at close range can you know what it's like.

"I know what you mean," Hartmut was saying. "It is a tremendous experience, and not just the first time either. Rocket firings never quite become routine. Their sound is always awesome. Now," he pointed toward P-7, "they'll disconnect the instrumentation and plumbing, drain any residual propellant from the tanks, collect cameras, check recorder charts to see if the test structure can go back for another missile. Not so glamorous as an actual firing, but quite important."

Suddenly, I could contain myself no longer.

"Hartmut, the red tape . . . you've got to cut it right now." We were clambering down from P-1, and two mechanics, overhearing me, looked up in surprise. I hardly noticed.

"This is what I've been waiting for," I continued. "Please call personnel again, will you?"

Hartmut nodded and smiled.

"And books, reports, test results, basic principles . . . I've got to catch up!"

Hartmut's smile widened to a grin, but he said nothing. To this day I am grateful to him for not spoiling that hour with sober realism. For the moment I was in the clouds, and was convinced that every minute lost from that moment on might have serious consequences for me, the project, the entire country.

"I cannot tell you a thing about it," I wrote Irmel that night, "but today was the most exciting day of my life. . . ."

4

WORK AND DISASTER

Next day I received formal assignment as a BGS project engineer in the Electrical Department. After what I had seen the day before, this news left me frustrated and uncertain. I phoned Hartmut.

"I wouldn't turn it down," he cautioned. "BGS is as good a place as any to start, and it will take you all over the facility. Meanwhile, keep your goal in mind and be patient."

He was right of course. Actually I knew little about Peenemünde, its organization, or its make-up. Learning all this while working in a field more familiar to me certainly had its advantages. And, it would have looked bad to change my mind after having given Maas my consent. Pacified, though still disappointed, I looked forward to the next morning.

The department head was Siegmund Mueller, a pleasant, congenial man. Mueller had been with AEG, a large industrial concern, for a long time, and had spent a number of years in China. Planning electrical power supply and distribution for large plants and industrial installations was his life's work. During the next few weeks I learned much from him.

BGS was divided into suitable departments which handled all major construction jobs at Peenemünde. I soon found myself on familiar ground, with work closely related to my activities at Siemens. The days flew by. I was working, really working again, and that was the important thing. Inspection trips to construction

50

areas, visits to pump stations, and discussions with subcontractors soon restored that peculiar fascination which is always a part of big construction jobs. Memories of the Russian front grew dim and distant.

But there were constant reminders that the war was on. Although no one took them very seriously in this area, air raid warnings were a regular occurrence—mostly at night. This region was a favorite rendezvous point for night bombers and was used as an alley for air raids on Berlin, which, incidentally, were being felt to an increasing degree throughout Germany.

"I am sorry to report this," I told Mueller one day, "but the pump stations 'Karlshagen Beach' and 'Village' won't be finished on schedule, if indeed they can be finished at all. The same holds true for the power distribution panels in F-1. Vital parts are overdue."

"What happened? I saw the shipping papers just a few days ago."

"Siemens called this morning. Another air raid two days ago knocked out their switch factory. They are evacuating machinery to emergency facilities outside of Berlin, but no one knows when they'll be back in business. And, there is no inventory whatsoever. It's been hand-to-mouth for a long time."

Mueller sighed. He had seen a lot of the world and had few illusions. He reached for a folder.

"I have been talking to Maas, and it's just the same with other hardware. Valves, for instance. But we're not through yet. There is the *Arbeitsfront*—Hitler's 'Worker's Organization'—we're going to raid Mukran."

He opened a folder and spread out a map of the eastern half of the nearby island of Rügen. Between the beach resorts of Sassnitz and Binz was a sizable area marked *KdF-Bad Mukran*. A sketch showed building plans and characteristic views. The name was familiar. At the outbreak of World War II, numerous gigantic government-sponsored construction projects had been in various stages of completion, including the monstrous buildings at Nuremberg, and the huge assembly halls along the "Axis" in Berlin. BGS had been involved in some of these projects, which, with the war, had all become dormant. Among the biggest was the one Mueller was talking about, the *Kraft durch Freude*— "Strength through Joy"—beach resort at Mukran, *KdF-Bad Mukran.*

"Look at it!" Mueller exclaimed. "One continuous building over a mile long. And it's almost finished—all the plumbing, all the power distribution is in. A real bonanza! Up to now nobody's been able to touch it—no matter how critical their defense need. But Maas helped design it, and has now finally gotten limited permission to remove some of the equipment. You're going to go there; select what we need; and arrange for its shipment. A man from Mr. Bohmann's pump group will go along to select valves."

By midafternoon Monday, August 16, 1943, our small party had reached Bergen, a small town in the heart of the charming island of Rügen. There we met a Herr Ahlgrimm, a representative of the group originally in charge of building Mukran.

Next morning Ahlgrimm drove us over narrow, winding roads, through dense beech-tree forests and gently rolling countryside, where the grain harvest was in full swing. Our first destination was the small seaside resort town of Binz, twelve miles to the east. There we stopped long enough to make reservations at the Hamburger-Hof Hotel and then headed north toward Mukran on a secondary highway.

Here, the coastline was sharply outlined by the steep chalk cliffs so characteristic of Rügen and the islands around southern Sweden. These were framed by dark green woods on top and intense blue sea below. Fluffy summer clouds floated above. In the distance *KdF-Bad* nestled against the cliffs like a long wall. As we approached, it gradually resolved itself into the features I had seen indicated in Mueller's plans. After some delay in locating the caretaker, we asked to be taken to the water pump and processing plant first.

The pump plant, rather like a castle, was located on top of a hill. According to our guides, it was almost ready for operation, except for a few missing parts which had never arrived. While my companion went into details of his needs with the others, I climbed to the flat roof.

Below, almost on the shore, stretching in both directions was the colossal *KdF-Bad*. It was a continuous building six stories high and nearly one-and-one-half miles long, constructed so that all rooms faced the sea. At regular intervals, a total of ten wings projected from the main building toward the sea, each wing widening to a circular tip. These wings housed the service facilities and, in the tip itself, right above the ocean, glassed-in dining rooms and indoor recreation facilities. In between the wings, the glittering Ruegen beach, famous for its wide swath of white sand, shimmered in the sun, waiting for vacationers who now might never come.

I turned at the sound of footsteps. Ahlgrimm had climbed up to join me.

"Quite a thing," he said, nodding toward the building. "So much effort, now just rotting away. And on top of everything else, you fellows are starting to plunder it."

He shook his head. He had been at Mukran since the beginning, and it was a big part of his life. I could understand his hatred for the war, but that both the war and *KdF-Bad* grew from the same root apparently had never occurred to him.

The rest of the day, Tuesday, August 17, we spent exploring the main building, cataloguing circuit breakers, distribution panels, and transformers—all of the things we so desperately needed at Peenemünde. Then, after a respectable meal in one of the few restaurants still operating in Binz and a leisurely stroll along the promenade in the warm summer dusk, we turned in. I fell asleep immediately.

Shortly after midnight a knock on the door awoke me. It was my companion from Peenemünde. I reached to turn on a light.

"Don't turn on your lights. Listen!" He hissed.

Then I heard it: the familiar rumbling drone of night bombers.

"Come out here. The hall window overlooks the sea."

I followed him out into the hall. The night was clear, and the moon, just past full, reflected from roofs and window panes. Buildings, streets, trees were clearly visible, almost as though in subdued sunlight. And there, out over the sea no more than 2,000 feet up were the bombers—a continuous, irregular stream of aircraft, droning relentlessly on in the night.

"The British," I murmured. "They always come by night. I wonder what they're after this time."

My companion shrugged. There were many targets in the direction in which they were flying: Berlin, Stettin, the synthetic gasoline plant. Besides, they never came in on a straight line, but used a distracting line of approach in order to confuse our night fighters.

"Peenemünde is in that direction too," I added as an afterthought.

"True, but they've passed over Peenemünde so often already, either they don't know it's there or they are waiting until the production facilities are ready. Well, we'll see. I just thought I'd warn you. I'm going back to bed. Good night."

The rumbling and thundering of the bombers continued for more than an hour. For a long while I could not get back to sleep. I felt a strange foreboding.

Next morning I awoke with the same feeling of apprehension.

"Try to get through by phone to Peenemünde," I told the Mukran caretaker. "See if they had any trouble."

Many hours later, during which we catalogued and prepared shipping schedules for the equipment we were taking away, the caretaker reported that he couldn't get through.

"Something must have happened along the line. Maybe it's Greifswald," he volunteered.

Greifswald? There's nothing they would want there. Apprehension grew into conviction. I told the caretaker to keep trying. We shook our heads and returned to work with renewed vigor. Then, late in the afternoon the caretaker came running up, breathless.

"One of the women here . . . her husband works for BGS . . . she got a call from him. He told her he had a job placing the call . . . finally had to phone from Anklam on the mainland."

We gathered around him. I'm afraid I shouted.

"What! What did he tell her?"

"He just wanted to assure her that he was all right. He didn't give her any details. All he said was that it looked pretty bad."

Peenemünde had been bombed. My associate and I looked at each other. Finally I broke the silence.

"All right. Let's wrap it up here." I turned to our host. "Mr. Ahlgrimm, please find out when we can make the earliest train connection in the morning, and pick us up in time to make it."

We were grim. My heart was hardly in my work, and I didn't sleep well that night. All the way back I kept wondering how badly Peenemünde had been hit, and what effect it would have on our work. I thought of the long stream of bombers the night before. How many were there? How accurate was their bombing?

I saw the first evidence of what had happened that afternoon as I walked across the bridge at Wolgast and entered the railroad station on the island side. A train had just pulled in from the east. The crowd was as dense as at rush hour, only now there were many, mostly men, with bandages, arms in slings, a man on crutches, and an unusual amount of luggage. It had the appearance of an evacuation. There was no time to stop and ask questions. Our train east was almost empty. Outside, the countryside was warm and green and peaceful. I viewed it with concern and impatience. How was Hartmut? What, I kept asking myself, had happened to the plant? Why didn't the train go faster!

The plant station at Zinnowitz was unusually crowded. As we passed through I picked up fragments of conversation. These people had had a terrible experience. My fears deepened. Then my companion noticed a friend from the plant. I forget his name.

"We're just back from a business trip. What happened? How does it look?"

The man shook his head uncertainly.

"The housing project was badly hit, and the railroad yard. I haven't been farther inside, but I understand some of the hangars are destroyed, and *Haus 4* has burned down."

"How about the people? Were there many casualties?" my companion asked somewhat hesitantly.

"I am afraid so, yes," the man nodded ruefully. "There is talk of a thousand or so dead. A lot of women and children. Most of the casualties were in Camp Trassenheide."

Then, with hurried apologies, he was gone.

The plant station, other than being busier than usual, appeared unchanged. Not so the train! Instead of the familiar *S-Bahn* cars, an old steam locomotive with a few run-down passenger cars awaited us. All the electric trains had been either completely destroyed or badly damaged, except one, which was in Zinnowitz during the raid. Even the latter could not be used, however, because of breaks in the overhead wire.

The first bomb craters appeared as we passed the WAAF building. Only a few, but the number steadily increased as we approached the plant. At times it had all the appearance of a tornado's aftermath—the woods were virtually flattened. So far, I noticed, all the destruction appeared to have been north of the tracks.

The houses of Trassenheide town came into view on the south; there were no signs of damage there. Just as we approached Camp Trassenheide itself, the ground on both sides of the track looked as though it had been worked over by a giant plow. Suddenly the train ground to a stop. A conductor moved through the cars, shouting that the track was broken here and that we would have to walk a few hundred yards up the line to another train.

I stepped out; the train had stopped just at the edge of the camp. The rows of barracks had been reduced to heaps of rubble; the few structures still standing only served to highlight the general destruction. For several hundred yards, the railroad bed had been torn up along the camp frontage, leaving shattered rails and ties clawing up into the air, twisted into weird and fantastic shapes. It looked as though the attackers had used the railroad track as a sort of ruler. Everything had been dropped north of it, with a few exceptions such as the camp area. For about the length of the camp, the fury of destruction had crossed over the track and had even torn up the highway paralleling it, along with a couple of nearby farmhouses.

Everywhere people were busy. Some were operating road-building equipment, preparing detours; others were digging, blasting, and torch-cutting as first steps in clearing the railroad bed.

The grimmest task of all was that of removing the victims from the camp. The bombs had struck while most of the people were asleep. Many apparently had tried to escape, but were caught while running. The gates of the chain-link fence, although open, were too far away for most, and many who tried to climb over the fence were killed as they climbed. Here and there the bombs had opened great gaps in the fence, destroying at the same time those hapless souls climbing to safety.

It was too early to establish the exact number lost, but estimates were that half of the one thousand or so inhabitants of the camp had been killed. Expediency did not permit elaborate methods of retrieving the bodies. Groups with stretchers shuttled between the wreckage and waiting trucks. On these, between latticed sidings and under tarpaulin roofs, bodies were being stacked like sacks of flour. Someone's grim sense of orderliness had determined that they all be placed with feet toward the inside, and heads poking out the rear. This presented a sickening sight of disarranged hair and dangling arms. We made our way slowly between bomb craters until we reached the intact portion of the track.

At the Siedlung station I left my companion and headed rapidly toward my quarters. The change was frightful. The serene and pleasant vista of green-shrouded "Siedlung" family houses was gone. Blast damage was visible everywhere, ranging from completely demolished buildings to shattered windows. It was clear that a great number of explosive bombs had been dropped. There were few signs of incendiary bombs.

However, I found the camp undamaged. In one spot only, in the northwestern quarter, was there any destruction. One of the single-story buildings had partially collapsed and debris, mixed with hastily rescued cots, closets, and other furniture items, was scattered around it. *Haus Württemberg* seemed deserted. I put in a phone call for Hartmut, and although I could not get hold of him I was relieved to find that he was all right.

I found my room in the same condition I had left it a few days before, except that my roommate had apparently moved out—all of his things were gone. I was simply too weary to ponder on this, so I stretched out to rest. A noise next door brought me to my feet, and I stepped out into the hall. I met one of my neighbors, about to leave.

"I just got back from my trip," I exclaimed. "I saw part of what happened as I came in. Where is everybody?"

"You missed a big show, but lucky you are!" He shrugged. "I honestly don't know where everybody is. I believe Major

Heigel of the VKN is trying to set up new headquarters in Zinnowitz. They've requisitioned some of the smaller hotels for the various companies. I met our Master Sergeant this morning. He suggested that I join them tonight. Unfortunately, I have different plans. I hope this thing blows the whole silly VKN club to pieces." He hoisted his bag. "Excuse me, I have to catch that train. She will never forgive me if I'm late. See you, Dieter."

Off he went. There was a brief noisy drumming of boots on the stairway, the door slammed, then footsteps faded away, and silence returned.

My hunger got the best of me, and I gave up the idea of a nap and went over to the service building. The kitchen was operating on a small scale, but the food was excellent, the entire stock being available for the few customers around. When I returned to the barracks about two hours later, I met two other company members in the hall. They had just returned from the housing project. Their stories were disheartening.

That night I was so exhausted I slept like a stone. The next morning I walked all the way over to *Werk Nord*. Near the military headquarters, a public address system was operating from a parked truck. I noticed a blond young man at the mike, who I learned was Wernher von Braun. I paused to look and listen for a moment, for this was the first time I had seen him. Announcements came from him in a continuous flow, carried by a clear, determined voice, spiced with an occasional humorous remark. In rapid succession the voice told us where Mr. Tessmann had set up his new office; that Foreman Becker's shop was untouched and no reason existed not to resume work; that building "TW" had been completely destroyed, and that those who had been working there should contact Mr. Schaefer on Extension 355; that Mr. Weidner and Mr. Heller were to report immediately to Dr. von Braun; and so on.

I could not linger; my immediate goal was the BGS and my office. A short walk around two corners nearby and it was clear that the BGS building no longer existed. Since it was one of the few wooden structures here, it had burned completely to the ground. A layer of ashes was all that was left.

It took me almost the entire day to find the scattered forces of the BGS. In small hotel rooms, in homes, and in provisional offices, the first plans for repairing the damage were already being laid out. I was immediately drawn into the vigorous effort. Within a few days, two abandoned barracks in the camp were converted to BGS offices, and work was proceeding, almost at a normal rate, different only in that all plans for new buildings were indefinitely stopped, except those for certain vital plant facilities.

During the following weeks I went through just about the entire plant, usually by bicycle, now the only reliable means of transportation. These trips were mostly in connection with the repair of some electrical system or transfer line; they eventually supplied me with a complete picture of the effects of the raid.

The test facilities in their entirety were unharmed; so was the Luftwaffe's *Werk West,* and hence their V-1 development was unhampered. The upper and part of the second story of *Haus 4,* engineering headquarters for V-2 development, had burned out. An auxiliary roof was soon in place, thereby reactivating almost the entire building. Two of the large hangars in the development plant were damaged beyond repair. There was localized damage here and there.

In *Werk Süd,* located between *Werk Nord* and the Housing Project, the still-unfinished office building and the adjacent temporary office barracks were completely lost. There had been a few hits, fortunately not serious, on F-1, the just-completed first unit of the production plant. Its immediate neighbor, *IW Süd,* Maintenance Shop South, had barely been scratched.

The question in everybody's mind in those days was not what *had* been hit, but rather what *had not* been hit and what the enemy might have intended to destroy. This was inevitably linked to a second problem: How well had the secret of the project been kept? After four years of war, security regulations were accepted and observed by the entire German population like nightfall, blackout, and going to sleep. By contrast, particularly to us newcomers, Peenemünde appeared to be wide open in this respect. Word had gotten around. Government propaganda about *Wunder-Waffen,* wonder weapons, was causing increasingly widespread speculation.

True, office procedures and handling of classified correspondence were as cumbersome and strict as could possibly be. The supervision of those matters and the punishment of security violators as a matter of fact provided an excellent opportunity for ambitious security officers. Otherwise, over-all plant protection and secrecy appeared inadequate.

There was a story about a Luftwaffe officer which made its point well. Without official authorization, the story went, this officer had driven to the V-1 launching site near Zempin, south of Zinnowitz; impressed the guard with his uniform and the pitch of his voice, a never-failing combination for the successful Prussian officer; waved an important looking but fake paper under his nose; and ordered a loaded V-1 transport vehicle hooked to his truck, which he drove off and promptly delivered to an embarrassed Luftwaffe security officer.

Our A-4 fuel trucks were literally Trojan horses. These were equipped with a hose compartment between the driver's cab and tank, which was enclosed and large enough to hold six men easily. As a result, they were frequently used for transportation. Yet I never saw a guard look inside that compartment! An entire army could have been smuggled into the plant or whole rocket sub-assemblies out.

There were thousands of people employed there, including over a thousand foreign laborers; half of German industry was under contract to us, in varying degrees; whole villages of the island's population were actually within the outer plant boundary; reconnaissance planes passed over almost daily; there were miles of waterfront with Swedish islands almost at rowboat distance. It seemed impossible to me that the enemy had not long since learned of our activities and of the detailed lay-out of the plant.

Yet the pattern of the attack did not indicate anything but a cursory knowledge of the plant's structure, and certainly no real understanding of the relative importance of its principal units. More than eighty per cent of the bombs in the raid had fallen on unoccupied areas, notably the woods; of the remainder, at least half had fallen into nonmilitary or nonindustrial areas, or onto readily repairable targets such as roads. The fact that, in spite of the apparent lack of detailed knowledge, the plant had been heavily, if unsystematically, damaged, illustrated to me the violence and scope of the attack. There was little doubt that the tonnage of explosives would have been sufficient to annihilate Peenemünde had it been well placed.

The official figures were summarized in a later report: 815 people had been killed, including some 600 foreign laborers. Approximately 600 four-engine bombers had dropped 10,000 one-thousand-pound explosive bombs and a large number of incendiaries. Simultaneous raids on a smaller scale had been made on subcontractor plant RAX in Vienna and DEMAG in western Germany. This was part of the effort to knock out Germany's secret weapons, known to the Allied world as "Operation Crossbow."

The raid resulted in a number of decisions. First, there would be no rebuilding which could be detected from the air. The Housing Project was completely evacuated, and the families living there were distributed over the northern portion of the island. Since most of the villages were resort areas, these refugees were easily absorbed. Certain administrative offices moved into some of the abandoned but still intact Project houses, and care was taken not to disturb the "aerial photogenicity" of the entire area.

Next, any plans to mass produce, or even pilot produce, at Peenemünde were abandoned. All the machinery being readied for that purpose was transferred to a subterranean plant at Niedersachswerfen, near Nordhausen, in central Germany. Here, the genial producer of the "Tiger" tank, Alwin Sawatzki, proceeded to perform another miracle in setting up A-4 mass production with little delay. His management of the program was so effective that the first mass-produced missiles arrived at Peenemünde for static firing and launching in early January, 1944—less than six months after the raid on Peenemünde.

Into the basement of the vacated F-1 hangar and into the nearby undamaged *IW Süd* moved those activities which had been bombed out of the development plant. Since test facilities and supporting plants, such as the liquid oxygen production plant, had been undamaged, development and assembly of test missiles, as well as their testing and launching, continued after only a brief interruption.

Numerous offices and laboratories were evacuated to hotels in the vacation sites south of the plant. In anticipation of a possible repeat raid, not only those which had been completely bombed out, but many others as well, were moved. Fictitious names were conceived for these locations, such as *Karlshagen 1* for Peenemünde, *Karlshagen 2* for Zinnowitz, *Karlshagen 4* for Koelpinsee, *Karlshagen 5* for Pudagla, and so on, named after the small hamlet of Karlshagen, near the plant entrance.

Immediately, construction was started on several sturdy air raid shelters, and, needless to say, air raid warnings were now taken seriously. Even reconnaissance planes were given full attention. All activity outside buildings froze when these planes passed over. This, combined with the basic rules of not visibly repairing significant damage and of parking vehicles under cover wherever possible, is what probably enabled us to continue the development of the V-2 without any further aerial interference for almost an entire year.

For some time prior to the raid, evacuation of Dr. Hermann's supersonic wind tunnel to another location had been considered. Thus, although it had been unaffected by the raid, this important facility was now moved to the area of Kochel, Bavaria, in a beautiful mountain setting. This tunnel was later brought to the U. S. where it is still in operation at the Naval Ordnance Laboratory, White Oak, Maryland.

The Army car pool authorities, who controlled the plant vehicles, decided to remove all of these vehicles from the plant every night, although automobile and truck losses had been slight. Depending on where the driver lived, this involved daily round trips up to fifty miles. While this provided convenient transportation for many train-weary commuters, it was hardly compatible with the gasoline situation at the time. It remained in force for more than a year.

The raid had one favorable effect on my own status. The VKN had evacuated to secondary hotels in Zinnowitz, and housing conditions were now such, that even the military people realized that squeezing four to six people into a 12-by-12-foot room was intolerable for men expected to perform a full day's professional work. As a result, permission to live in individual rented rooms wherever available was reluctantly granted to engineers and scientists being retained in uniform. When I told Hartmut about this a few days after my return from Ruegen, he said:

"Well, congratulations! Where are you going to put up your tent?"

"I like Koserow. I thought I'd look around there first."

"It just so happens that I know about a nice room for rent, a few blocks from our house. Why don't you drop in tonight and I'll introduce you to the people?"

"I'm afraid that won't be possible. The order is not official yet. Our company is presently housed in a barn on the mainland and they intend to bring us out there by truck in the evening."

"Oh, that's simple. Private First Class Huzel, you are hereby ordered to report for a technical discussion in the quarters of Lieutenant Kuechen in Koserow, tonight at 8 o'clock sharp. No excuses."

August 21 was a bright, sunny Saturday—but it was a sad day. Early in the morning, those who had died in the air raid were buried. A small cemetery had been cleared along the plant railroad tracks, north of Camp Trassenheide. Most of the victims, unidentified, had been placed in common graves. A few single graves had been set aside for Dr. Walter Thiel and his family, and others from the Housing Project.

A brief, dignified ceremony was conducted. The remainder of what in peacetime had been Zinnowitz' Kurkapelle-Promenade Concert Band, were dressed in somber dark blue suits and caps, together with a small choir played and sang chorales. A Catholic priest and a Protestant pastor delivered sermons.

Three days later came the first of many massive air attacks on Berlin that were virtually to destroy this lovely city, all but wiping out its southern suburbs. My fears for Irmel's safety mounted with each passing day.

5

ON THE PAD

The following days were occupied with setting up the new BGS offices in abandoned barracks of Camp Karlshagen. As soon as we were back in business, we had our hands full with repair work: restoring floor space under emergency roofs with no external modification, and reconstruction of minor damage which did not change the external appearance of the buildings. Considerably more effort was expended on power lines, cables, and railroad tracks. Roadwork was restricted to the most vital requirements.

Soon the rumor began to circulate that, in order to make up for the delay incurred by the raid and subsequent rebuilding, development of advanced missile models was to be stopped and effort concentrated on the final development of the A-4 and its smaller brother, the *Wasserfall*—Waterfall. The latter, technically the C-2, was a winged anti-aircraft rocket, launched vertically like the A-4, which could be directed to targets from the ground by joystick-operated radio transmitter systems. Also to be continued, according to the rumor, was the development of a small salvo-launch-type anti-aircraft rocket known as the *Taifun*.

Unlike so many rumors in big operations such as Peenemünde, this one was well-founded. It was most likely this concentration of effort that was responsible for Hartmut Kuechen's dropping in at my BGS office some time later.

"Imagine," he burst out after a short greeting, "I have just been appointed Engineer in Charge of P-7! I need an engineering assistant. Would you be interested?"

64

"Would I be interested? What a question! Of course I would."

Finally! Here was the break I had been seeking, sooner than I had dared hope. Such an assignment would bring me right into the heart of the experimental rocket development, in the largest and most complete facility in the whole plant. Then it struck me. My joy turned to chagrin. Mueller had since left BGS to take an appointment as a member of the National Development Advisory Board. With his departure, I had assumed some of his responsibilities. Hartmut's offer was what I had been dreaming of, but now I felt certain BGS would not release me. I expressed my fears to Hartmut. He grinned.

"Well, we'll have to do some fast talking. I discussed it with von Braun, and gave him a convincing story of your abilities. He has agreed to talk to Maas about it. Maas is a tough one to deal with, I know. So call me when he comes in tomorrow morning. We'll come on over in a surprise attack."

Early next morning, I called as planned. A few minutes later, Hartmut and von Braun arrived from *Haus 4*. Hartmut, I noted, waited outside Maas' office while von Braun went in. In a little while I was called in. This was the first time I had gotten a close look at von Braun. He greeted me with great friendliness, shaking hands with a firm clasp. Because of the unpredictably rainy weather we had been experiencing lately, he was wearing the inevitable Peenemünde leather topcoat, nonchalantly unbuttoned. He looked younger than I thought he should, blond and blue-eyed, with a full, strong-jawed face. While Maas continued the discussion, von Braun reclined in an armchair and looked at me with a curious, childlike, innocent stare, beaming and benevolent.

Maas appeared to be somewhat irritated. He talked to me in a hurt manner, and I began to feel rather guilty. It had just been a few days since I had finally gotten permission from the VKN to wear civilian clothes. This was the first time Maas had seen me without uniform. I had done this deliberately, since I knew it would deny him the psychological advantage unconsciously used by some civilians in supervisory positions at Peenemünde.

I suddenly realized that I had not been paying full attention to what Maas was saying. I brought myself back in time to hear him say that he thought I had been looking for another position because of lack of advancement in his organization, and possibly for salary reasons. I assured him truthfully that this was not the case, but that I felt very much attracted by the new work which had been offered me.

Politely but firmly, von Braun cut in.

"I certainly appreciate your cooperation in this matter, Mr. Maas. I think we are in agreement, then, that Mr. Huzel will start next week on a fifty-fifty basis until you've broken in a replacement. Well, I have to be on my way. Thank you again, very much indeed."

He rose abruptly. Smiling, he shook hands with both of us and left, leaving behind a Maas who hadn't said yes, but hadn't had time to say no, either.

My transfer met with no further difficulties, and in the weeks immediately following, I became more and more absorbed in my new assignment. Whereas before the whole Peenemünde complex at one time or another required my attention, virtually all my professional activities now were concentrated at test stand P-7, where earlier I had viewed my first static firing of an A-4 missile. The dominant feature of this area was, of course, the big assembly and preparation hangar where I had seen my first missiles. On clear days its massive face could be seen from the cliffs of Koserow ten miles away. It had been designed to handle not only the A-4, but the much taller A-9/A-10 two-stage intercontinental missile with which Hitler had at one time hoped to bombard the United States. This missile was never built, and in fact development had by then been abandoned in order to concentrate all effort on the A-4. It was to have consisted of the A-10 booster of 440,000 pounds thrust, and the A-9, essentially a winged A-4, as the final sustainer stage with 56,000 pounds thrust. This concept was similar to the boost-glide vehicle first proposed by Dr. Eugen Sänger in the mid-1930's and now under development in the United States as the Dyna-Soar boost-glide hypersonic bomber.

P-7's nerve center was the control building positioned astride the earthen wall surrounding the test arena. Here were the offices of the engineer in charge and his engineering staff. In a large room with windows facing away from the arena, fifteen staff engineers had their desks. Usually these were deserted, since the engineers spent most of their time at the site preparing tests, following up malfunctions, checking out systems, etc. At the far end of the office was a smaller room closed off by a glass partition. Here, Hartmut had his desk, and my own was placed against it. Adjacent, a second pair of desks was occupied by Helmut Klee, our administrative assistant, and Willi Muenz, our very capable lead test engineer.

The routine (which it rarely was) at P-7 can best be described by taking a typical day—November 8, 1943, the month of the Teheran meetings when the invasion of France was agreed to. Fall was already well upon us, and the few deciduous trees scattered among the conifer groves added their vivid colors to our evergreen environment. Rain was frequent, and on such days everything was drab; the flat wooded landscape, the sky, and the sea all merging into a dull gray equanimity. When the cold damp winds blew in from the water outside, work was difficult for personnel, and hard on delicate test equipment. Today was such a day.

Hartmut and I had just finished reviewing the action plans for the next week, when Muenz entered, slumped in his chair and sighed with relief.

"Well, we finally made it. The last checkout was O.K. A cold solder spot in the main distributor box again. Took them all night to run it down." He turned toward me. "They're closing the instrument doors, Mr. Huzel. We'll be moving the cucumber into the arena right away. If you want to observe the loading procedure . . ."

Test Vehicle V-43, after several static firings, had just gone through final preflight checkout in the hangar. This consisted first of checking out the mechanical portion of the propulsion system: pumps, valves, mixture control orifices, leak-checks, etc. Also, the propulsion group had installed new graphite vanes in the combustion chamber nozzle, replacing those that had been worn during static tests.

Then Guidance and Control, BSM, had checked out their systems. A hundred times that morning I had heard the starting whine of one of the small motor-generators in the missile nose compartment. Signals were fed into the system, rudder and vane deflections measured, response times recorded, potentiometers adjusted. All this activity was accompanied by nearly unintelligible shop talk.

"Oehmig-2 is running."

"Messina-1 is not yet connected."

"Hold off installation of the dummy elephant until we've replaced the Honnef."

"We don't have continuity; probably those confounded fly-legs again."

And so it went, the many countless things that have to be done prior to launch—all attended to with the loving and determined care of ladies-in-waiting preparing a princess for her wedding. This was a business that never lost its fascination and dedication.

When I entered the hangar, mechanics were just screwing a large lifting eye into V-43's nose tip. "V" stood for *Versuch*— test—and the following number indicated assembly, rather than test sequence. V-73, for example, would follow V-43 to P-7's launch stand.

The nose cone, which bore the nickname "elephant," was shaped exactly like the actual warhead, but was filled with one metric ton of sand instead of explosive. Now an overhead crane meticulously engaged the eye and slowly, while men on the floor held the boattail against swaying, moved the missile into the waiting arms of a *Meiller-Wagen,* which gripped it and gently lowered it into the horizontal position. While this process was underway, the great hangar doors slid aside, and a tractor backed in, hooked onto the *Meiller-Wagen,* and began moving the whole load out of the hanger. Guided by much shouting and arm-waving, the tractor entered the arena through the tunnel-like gateway. Here, in an elegant maneuver, the *Meiller-Wagen* was backed to within a few feet of the launching platform. With wire rope and winch, it was carefully snaked into engagement with the table and latched firmly to it.

The erector arm went up again with a whir and righted the missile directly over the launch table. A few turns of the four heavy levelling screws below the fins, and the rocket was entirely supported by the table. The straps holding it to the erector arm were released, and the wagon crawled away.

For a moment V-43 stood alone, majestic and unencumbered. Then quickly a tower-like wooden structure, open on one end, containing working platforms at various levels and slotted to receive the missile, moved up on rails to completely enclose the rocket. On these platforms, the last checkouts—essentially to do with guidance and control—were soon underway. Then, the announcement:

"All clear for fueling!"

Tank trucks backed and maneuvered into position. Lines were hooked up, and pump motors started. First, alcohol filled the smaller upper tank. Then, liquid oxygen started to flow into the lower tank, accompanied by the complaining noise of the cold and the creeping line of hoarfrost. Tanking accomplished, the trucks pulled away, and the rail-mounted checkout tower lumbered rattlingly aside.

By now "X-time" was only a few minutes away, time to retreat to the protection of the control center. I entered from the arena through two heavy steel doors, the innermost of which, incidentally, I never saw closed. There were still only a few people in the control room. One man stood at the propulsion console; another hovered over the guidance panel. Both wore headsets connecting them to the intercom. Periodically one or the other would repeat an order, flip a switch or twist a valve control, and repeat the order back in confirmation. Occasionally one would step to one of the four periscopes in the control room and check some element of the activity around the missile. The big X-time clock in the arena read "X minus four minutes."

As I watched, engineers entered and took readings from instruments lining the walls, then departed, scribbling in their notebooks. The whole atmosphere was relaxed; everything was going just as it should, very professionally.

As the arena was evacuated, more and more people drifted into the control room. Most went right on through: back to work in the hangar, or to climb to the hangar roof to watch the launch. Most of the test site crew would gather in front of the control center. During static firings, some brave souls even climbed on the arena wall for a closer view. The actual launching crew often remained in the open tunnel adjacent to the control center.

When the last man had cleared the arena, the control room door was closed. Its shatter-proof window provided a view of the arena, before which was stationed an observer in direct telephone communication with the Telemetering Building. There, devices were installed which received signals from the missile in flight, converted them into missile speed, digested them, and then sent the cutoff signal when the speed required to achieve a certain range had been obtained. This was called the Wolman System, named after its developer.

I started to ask the observer something about the test procedure and then changed my mind. He was a very busy man at that moment.

"Come again," he said into the mouthpiece of his telephone, "I didn't hear you." After a pause, "Okay, I'll tell him. He won't like it though." He put the receiver down and went into the control room.

"Where is Muenz?" I heard him ask. "Oh, there you are. Bruetzel just called. He can't give you an all clear. Steinhoff hasn't arrived yet. He's bringing some visitors. Bruetzel said to tell you that Steinhoff and the brass left Pudagla some time ago, and ought to be here any minute. He says to stand by."

I looked in. Muenz, wearing a resigned, almost bored expression, was putting his headset down. He swore and stamped by me, out of the building, and lit a cigarette.

Ten minutes later, the word came: "All clear. Proceed with launching." Muenz came back in, his expression still resigned, and put his headset back on. The engineers scurried to their stations.

"Sound the two-minute siren," said Muenz.

The shriek of the undulating siren was muffled by the three feet of concrete over our heads.

"Close arena door."

"Arena door is closed."

"Turn key to launch." Muenz spoke firmly but calmly.

"Key is on launch."

Muenz was looking intently through the periscope as he issued these instructions. He nodded easily at their confirmation from the man at the propulsion console. Finally he turned toward the operator.

"You have the all-clear light?"

"All clear is on."

"Are photographers on station?"

Confirmation came through the headset. "Pressurize A-tank."

The man at the console turned a rotary switch. A voice sang out, "Vent valve is closed." Then another: "A-tank pressurizing: point five, point eight, one atmosphere, one point two, A-tank pressurized."

"Is BSM clear?"

There was silence. Muenz turned. "Is BSM clear?" he repeated.

There was a worried look on the face of the BSM console operator. Several times he threw a particular switch; at last he turned, an unspoken request for assistance. A guidance engineer joined him and they both studied the dials. There was a quick exchange of questions and answers, in subdued voices and with intercom mikes turned aside. Then they went over to the power supply and distribution panel at the rear wall; more discussion as they scanned the instruments and checked switch positions. Finally the guidance engineer straightened and pronounced sadly:

"Oehmig invertor No. 2 is shot. We'll have to replace it."

"Oh, hell," said Muenz, taking off his headset. "Turn launch key off," he concluded.

The X-time clock, already on plus 15 minutes, was set back to minus two hours.

Muenz went out front for a smoke, again wearing that resigned, almost bored expression. He had good reason to be unhappy. Once the liquid oxygen had been tanked, it was important that the launching proceed without delay. Cold air from the tank and from the oxygen pump would soon cool all the hardware in the boattail to temperatures far below freezing. Moisture condensing and freezing on metal surfaces, valve stem bushings, and electrical harnesses increased the chances of a malfunction. The only solution was draining, warming up, and drying the missile—in other words, starting all over again. Almost two hours later, BSM reported:

"All clear. Hope the other Oehmigs will last. They've been on for quite a while."

Muenz, still waiting outside the control center, did not reply. He turned to the crew chief.

"Did you replenish the liquid oxygen?"

"Yes. The truck just left. The housing is gone; we're ready to go."

"Okay, let's get moving then." Muenz threw a half-finished cigarette to the ground and went back into the center.

Once again he directed the same sequence of operations, calmly, self-assured, unruffled.

"Now. Is BSM clear?"

"BSM all clear."

"Wolman clear?"

"All clear," said the observer.

"Well, here goes. Smoke bomb! Siren!"

Again there came the brief, muted wail of the siren. The smoke bomb was simultaneously released from the arena wall. Although I could not see it from within the center, I had many times before watched it race its wriggly green scrawl of smoke 100 feet into the air, a sight which more than one uninformed observer had taken as some form of missile malfunction.

A moment later, Muenz yelled, "Ignition!"

I had managed to acquire a periscope position. Through the lens I saw the bright flash of the hydrazine and hydrogen peroxide flame spread from the rocket nozzle, sparkling and intense. The bringing together of these two hypergolic—self-igniting—chemicals was still our method of ignition; it was not until later that we adopted a pinwheel pyrotechnic igniter.

"Pre-stage."

"Pre-stage on."

A new flame—yellowish-orange, painfully brilliant—shot out, eating up the ignition flame, swirling violently, sweeping the launching table and deflector and the surrounding earth like a giant broom of fire. In seconds it had steadied itself.

"Pre-stage okay."

"Main stage."

I glanced quickly to the side, in time to see the operator turn the rotary switch. But nothing new happened. Muenz still had his eyes glued to the periscope and, suspecting a misunderstanding, he repeated, very loudly: *"Main stage!"*

"Main stage is on!" responded the operator, equally loudly.

"Cutoff," said Muenz wearily.

The pre-stage flame disappeared. There was a momentary, lingering after-fire. A huge white cloud shot out of the oxygen tank vent line, then thinned to the usual standby plume of vapor. Muenz resumed his resigned air.

"Report to the Telemetering Building: Main stage didn't take. Probably a frozen control valve. We'll have to drain the tank. No test today."

He paused, cursed, and took off his headset. Something of his phlegmatic expression was reflected in the faces of everyone there. Outside, he lit a cigarette and stared moodily into the sky as he smoked.

There were days like that. But there were better days, too. This was why there were test programs and test engineers. As our knowledge grew and our techniques and our product improved, the troubles and the bad days became fewer.

The next day, launching preparations followed the same routine. True to Muenz' theory, the trouble had been a frozen control valve. It had been warmed, dried, and found to be in perfect order.

I decided this time to view the launching from outside. When the firing crew left the arena, I followed them through the control room to the front of the building, where smoking was permitted. Here the atmosphere was relaxed and usually remained that way until the last siren sounded.

Inside the control center, of course, the tension would mount noticeably as the launching sequence moved closer and closer to main stage. In fact, there have been very few occasions in my life when I have felt as tense and on edge as when in charge of a launching. Static firings, by comparison, always seemed mild. Some of the others would argue that the two events are really entirely the same, short of the fact of actually letting the missile go.

Logically it was true, but it just didn't seem to work out that way. If nothing else, your pulse rate in the two different circumstances told the difference.

We passed a few minutes in small talk, until finally the siren sounded.

"Two minutes," someone remarked.

Conversation died and we moved into the tunnel. From a point about halfway inside, the entire rocket was in full view. It looked so peaceful and isolated from a distance of 250 feet! Only the white plume of vapor drifting up from the oxygen tank vent line moved.

Again the siren sounded, briefly; then the thud of the smoke bomb; and in quick succession, ignition and pre-stage. An irregular rumbling filled the air. Orange flame swept the ground in all directions, stirring up dust that mixed furiously with the white clouds of steam rising from the puddles of flush-water surrounding the launching table. The layer of frost clinging to lines and tank cascaded down and was caught up in the swirling air currents until a miniature blizzard surrounded the engine and launching table.

Suddenly the two cable connectors leading from the tall mast dropped from the instrument compartment high up near the nose of the missile, swung widely to the side, and arced down into a net. Almost simultaneously, the flame at the missile tail began to build up at a tremendous rate—thirtyfold in less than a second, to be exact. The violence of the jet threw the gas and dust in billowing clouds clear to the arena walls and high up into the air. A blast of hot air rushed down the tunnel. Out of this churning cloud, the rocket slowly rose, surely the most thrilling sight I have ever seen. It is difficult to describe the sound; it virtually filled the air, tangible, powerful, a crescendo of noise. You not only heard it, you felt it, a vibration that shook your whole body.

Immediately at lift-off, those around me dashed forward to the arena end of the tunnel, in order not to lose sight of the ascending rocket. I followed, a little apprehensively; after all, I was still a novice. Peeking out from the tunnel exit, I saw the A-4 at a steep angle overhead. Its jet, now unrestricted by deflectors, was a narrow, glowing plume the length of the missile itself. Almost translucent where it emerged from the thrust chamber, it graduated into a bright yellow-orange at the tip. The roar had changed in pitch; crisp overtones were present. I saw the sense of the common saying that a rocket is a sustained explosion.

The sound began to abate. By now the men from the control center had also come outside, and stood with their heads tilted back like the rest of us. Some peered through binoculars.

The rocket was now about a thousand feet and had already started to tilt over in a northeasterly direction.

"The trajectory program has started," remarked the engineer behind me. Everybody assured everybody else of the fact. This was the signal to step further into the arena, away from control room doors and tunnel. The possibility of the rocket falling back into the launching area no longer existed.

Soon the sound of the rocket was so distant that conversation could be carried on at a normal volume.

Suddenly, as if drawn by a giant hand, a bold chalk mark appeared, on the canvas of the blue sky. The rocket had entered a layer of cooler air, causing the formation of a vapor trail. "There's the condensation mark," I heard from half a dozen different engineers almost simultaneously. It seemed to be a final confirmation that all was well.

As abruptly as it had started, the vapor trail stopped. I lost track of the missile at that moment. While I was searching vainly for it, the vapor trail slowly distorted, twisted, disintegrated, and finally dissolved. Then there was another brief burst of vapor trail. Then again, it was gone. Someone yelled,

"Cutoff—63 seconds."

The engine had stopped, but the distant rumbling was still clearly audible, undulating as it faded. It continued for perhaps another two minutes, until the last sound wave from the cutoff point, some 23 miles away from where we stood, reached our ears.

Cutoff speed was around 3500 miles an hour. It had now entered the silent ballistic phase of its flight. In the same sense that accurate training of the gun and the correct weight of the powder charge are important if the shell is to hit the target, so the rocket's speed, location and attitude, its orientation in space, at cutoff are essential to the trajectory. All these factors are closely controlled by intricate electronic devices.

To mark the exact point of impact with the water, these test missiles carried bags filled with an intense green dye which left a clearly visible stain on the surface of the sea. This stain lasted long enough for a search plane to mark the location and complete the triangulation. As a rule, the first scattered information would come in on the day of the launching: range, side deviation, cutoff data. A small telemetering set rode some of the missiles, transmitting selected data and the signals of position-gyroscopes describing the rocket's true attitude in space. A receiver was set up in a lighthouse near Koserow.

The oscillograph traces from the telemetering transmission were developed at the lighthouse. The graph, which was several hundred feet long, was suspended through the center hole of the circular staircase, hanging freely for drying—certainly a strange sight! Those interested in particular events of the missile's flight would climb up and down the spiral steps to look at the applicable portions of the graph paper. How different it all seems today, when the oscillograph records of engine firings and missile launchings are developed, dried, and folded into neat packages by precision automatic machines, within minutes after the conclusion of the test.

The launching platform was being inspected as I left the arena after the official all-clear signal. Somehow, I have always had a peculiar feeling at the sight of an empty launching table following a launching. A product of our efforts was missing. Only a few minutes before it had been there, and now we would never see it again.

"Well, that closes the books on V-43," said Muenz. There was an undertone of satisfaction in his voice. Then he turned away from me and began to look after the progress of V-73, which was to be launched the next day.

6

THE SUPER-ENGINEER

"We here are super-engineers!"

I will never forget those words, spoken to me by a young enthusiast shortly after my arrival at Peenemünde. My first impressions of the shops and design offices, the test stands, and the launching pads, were still fresh, and his words seemed to confirm my romantic concept of rocketry and space travel. After all, hadn't I grown up on colorful lectures by people like Max Valier, and on even more glamorous science fiction novels of those fantastic push-button devices, controlled by superhuman tycoons conversing casually in differential equations?

As my familiarity with Peenemünde grew, those words kept popping into my mind. For a while, I suppose, I thought that someday I would develop into one of those "super-engineers" myself. I admired from a distance those whom I believed had already achieved this higher order of existence—from the obscure language, the secrecy that seemed to shroud their actions, and from the occasional "private notebook" tactics that some of them used. It was only very gradually that I learned that the only thing that could be called superhuman here was the effort that everyone had to contribute, day in and day out, in the face of failure upon failure, to bring into the world an entirely new branch of science. There wasn't a single super-engineer in the entire plant, it turned out—just believing, stubborn, undaunted, hard workers. There were those days when nothing seemed to go right, when on top of all the mechanical trouble a directive would come through to transfer some key personnel to another facility, supposedly suffering even more than we from the acute shortage of skilled manpower, or when an urgent request for a "progress" report would be received at a time when we felt that we had made about everything but that! Or when a simple need like a few two-by-four's could not be filled for days, holding up some vital construction project. Or proper protective clothing, or a hot meal for the night crew—or a hundred such things.

Then all of us would realize again that there was no super-engineering, just the miracle of the human mind, which, given unshaken belief, untiring effort, ingenuity, hard work, dedication, is capable of solving almost anything. And above all, there was the indescribably wonderful feeling when finally there was success, erasing within a few seconds the drudgeries of many months, and supplying the will to strive through yet more failures.

Still today, many years later, I think there is a little bit of Walter Mitty in every rocket engineer—that work is still shrouded by an air of mystery and is characterized by dreamlike visions and a belief in miracles just around the corner. Some of this no doubt stems from the inherent need for secrecy; some of it, too, from not-always-realistic publicity; but most of it, I am sure, comes from man's natural curiosity and restless urge to new frontiers, his constant desire to learn what's above, below, on either side, and beyond.

One can assume that there was a time, thousands of years ago, when it was possible for one man to know everything worth knowing. There may have been no problem for the Neanderthal man, but times have changed. The German Gottfried Leibniz, who lived around 1700, is often regarded as the last polyhistor having been skilled in and having contributed to every then-known branch of science. Since then it has become increasingly difficult for any man to achieve full control of one science, or even a small subdivision of just one science. In rocketry, the scientist and engineer, more often than not, must admit to ignorance, puzzlement, and uncertainty. They have left behind the solid but narrow foundation of basic research.

Danger lies in this all-too-often forgotten fact. The young rocket engineer, even sometimes the not-so-young engineer entering rocketry, expects that many of the less glamorous realities that apply to human effort throughout the world, by some magic, no longer apply in the field of rocketry. Unlimited means exist, they think, with no red tape, no bothersome administrative chores, no stresses, no disappointments, no human relations problems: a big happy family of—here the concept again!—*super-engineers*.

This is dangerous because it can lead to disappointed restless men, conscious of the deceiving greener pasture nearby and forgetful of the truly great final goal. The result is a turnover rate that sometimes rocks this young and promising industry, breaking up research teams, throwing away experience worth billions of dollars, causing needless repetition and duplication of effort.

Dangerous it is too, because sometimes those at the other end of the scale—contracting agencies—equally do not realize what it has taken to build an effective team. Not grasping this, they permit haphazard reassignments, "economy" cancellations, so spreading further the fallacy that the science of rocket propulsion is something anyone can pick up overnight, and unnecessarily emphasizing that it is a highly speculative business besides.

Fortunately Peenemünde was spared much of this. For one, we were the first. We were pioneering a new industry, and each new success with a war missile only served to confirm our dreams of orbiting spacecraft, interplanetary travel, and manned exploration of the galaxy after the war. The resulting team spirit combined with the general fact that European industry, even in peacetime, is less plagued by turnover than American industry promoted stability. Other factors also worked toward this end: government decrees making job changes very difficult (by virtue of the threat of being drafted into the military); and the fact that many of the professional people had already had a taste of the life of a *Landser* on the fighting front.

It is also true that the pace, fascination, and significance of our work made us less conscious of the actual fact of the war. No matter how rough the hours—we often worked around the clock—and no matter how difficult the handicaps of wartime shortages, bureaucratic meddling, vacillating priorities, and repeated technological failure, almost to a man, we at Peenemünde figured we probably had it better than those poor souls in the big cities to whom the propaganda of inevitable victory was no longer an opiate, and those tired, shaken, weary soldiers on the fighting fronts who even more must have felt the onset of inevitable doom.

By the middle of 1943 Allied bombing of Germany could only be described as constant, heavy, and crippling. Over 30,000 people had died in one raid on Hamburg alone. Since August, Berlin itself had been under constant and severe attack. North Africa was lost, and in September the Italian government had capitulated to the Allies. It was only a matter of time now until the German armies in the east were shoved out of Russia and Poland. Reports of Allied invasion forces building up in Britain were persistent and could not be denied. At Peenemünde, critical parts and supplies became increasingly difficult to get; raids on our technical staff became more frequent and troublesome, but these things were purely relative. Since July, Hitler himself had been convinced that the A-4 would turn defeat into victory. We enjoyed the highest priorities and, unfortunately, increasing bureaucratic interest by propaganda and production experts. It was a result of this interest by the Propaganda Ministry that the A-4 became the V-2, *V* for *Vergeltung*—retaliation. It was first applied to the V-1 buzz-bomb on June 16, 1944, the day after the first four had dropped on London.

At times we felt the red tape, the "paper war," would strangle us. Having had considerable experience since then in other countries, I am convinced that we didn't have it so bad after all, particularly in view of scarcities, wartime regulations, etc. Noteworthy also was the nearly complete absence of Nazi party uniforms, party lapel buttons, and party activities in general. That we had bureaucracy was, of course, inevitable. But no one can seriously contend that it was a major deterrent to success of our mission. Our record proves it: *Two-and-one-half years between the first experimental launching of this completely novel vehicle and the launching of the last of over 4,000 operational vehicles.*

But it was never easy. If there were technical difficulties that strained the so-called state of the art, there were also times that tried the mettle of the men of Peenemünde, for above all this was a place of human beings. Many were the occasions when the stresses, the shortages, the interference seemed beyond endurance, when the "super-engineer" seemed not merely an exaggeration but an outright frivolity. There were days when even the toughest minds seemed to run out of resources, only to bounce back full of new ideas, drive, and enthusiasm—often after a long and sleepless night. This is a characteristic of a true leader: to recover from the shock of failure with new enthusiasm.

Our Test Section was no exception. There was the ever-present transportation problem, in my estimation the most severe of all. Everything was lacking: proper vehicles, gasoline, tires, spare parts. Yet we managed. Hartmut was a master. "Organizing" was only one of his talents, which included perseverance, lobbying, persuasion, and just plain selling. And so it was throughout Peenemünde. Parts on order would be delayed; might never be delivered. Standard practice became: "If it's not in stock, make it right here in the test shops. Improvise!"

I am grateful to the good fortune that assigned me first under Mueller and then under Hartmut, who was not only my boss but friend. His job was not easy. Personalities of vastly different backgrounds were packed in close association. There were differences of opinion within his organization as well as the constant problem of dealing with and satisfying higher-ups. Many of those who had advanced rapidly to positions of higher administrative authority just couldn't let go of the "nuts-and-bolts" matters with which they had been previously concerned. This was reflected in the Test Section's weekly "Monday meetings." It was difficult for Test Section Chief Dr. Martin Schilling to keep close to the actual day-to-day engineering activity of his large and complex operation and still sort out the constant flow of problems and questions from above.

Schilling had taken over Dr. Thiel's work as Test Section Chief after the latter's death, with Gerhard Heller assisting in continuing Thiel's engineering work. Schilling's background was typical of the Peenemünde engineer. Following graduation and acquisition of his doctorate, he had worked in a German university laboratory in the general field of applied physics. From there he had come to Peenemünde as an assistant to Dr. Thiel. His industrial experience was limited.

I met and talked with Schilling many times on his frequent

visits to P-7. He always came in his little Mercedes, with a chauffeur, and invariably wore a mackinaw. Of all the people of rank and name he was the only one without the customary leather overcoat. Hartmut was often out following up some problem or other, and on these occasions Schilling and I had many long conversations.

Usually we talked about things only loosely connected with our immediate work. Schilling's remarks were spiced with sarcasm, and he used pointed humor to illustrate his thoughts. To himself, at least, he admitted his limited industrial background and tactfully left such matters to those more adept in this field. He had a fundamental common sense and understood the difficulties associated with operation of such a large facility. He appreciated the difficulties generated by the presence of the guidance and control group, and also our critical need for additional equipment and outside assistance.

One Saturday afternoon, Hartmut said to me:

"I won't be in next Monday. Please sub for me at the Monday meeting. Klee will be along to help with the figures."

Monday came and, accompanied by Klee, I entered Schilling's office in *Haus 4*. It was a large, well-appointed room, partly wood paneled, and carpeted. Several of the engineers in charge of various other test facilities were already there—seated in chairs, leaning against the wall. Schilling sat behind a desk placed diagonally in one corner. He was a man about 32 years old, slender, with an intelligent face and close-set, somewhat piercing and restless eyes. He leafed through some papers until the last of us had arrived. Then he looked up, made a quick count of those present, and opened a large notebook.

"Well, let's get started," he announced. "Everyone seems to be here. We'll begin with Test Stand P-8."

P-8 was a combustion chamber calibration firing facility utilizing a pressurized propellant feed, rather than the A-4's regular turbopump system. Skillful, well-trained crews combined with sound planning had resulted in an impressive frequency of something like ten firings per shift.

Schilling took notes and occasionally asked questions, tying them in with the previous week's notes, while regarding the speaker in a friendly, encouraging manner. Occasionally he inserted pieces of information from the recent staff meeting, talking rapidly, easily, in a crisp voice. As time went on he warmed up noticeably, and his discourses grew more enthusiastic.

Suddenly he turned toward Klee and myself. He had been impressed by the P-8 report. Among other things, it would help his own report to those higher up. Our story would seem somewhat pale by comparison.

"What about P-7?" he inquired.

Klee calmly opened his notebook. He was reporting some detail of our previous week's engine system activities, which, as usual, involved numerous troubles and delays, when Schilling cut in.

"Are those fellows in the hangar still holding their ten o'clock siesta? Whenever I come to the test stand they seem to be having a break."

There was a ripple of laughter.

"No," replied Klee casually, "they finally gave up since you didn't send those couches you promised us last time."

Everyone, including Schilling, joined in the burst of laughter. Klee continued his report, periodically interrupted by Schilling's spiced remarks—for which he seemed to have an inexhaustible and oft-quoted vocabulary. As Klee intoned his monotonous data, my thoughts drifted. The voices of the meeting faded as I reflected on the real story behind Peenemünde.

Little over a year had elapsed since the first A-4 launching. The necessary know-how had been accumulated in a few years. There had been no previous effort with which to compare, no source-book of information. Within a short period, against tremendous difficulties, this rocket had been conceived, designed, built, developed, and launched. Our test effort was a last, important, and successful link in this chain. Static firings were now being conducted at P-7 at the rate of almost two a day, with actual launchings averaging one every two days. This was not accomplished without considerable effort above and beyond administrative work schedules.

Many of us at P-7 put in innumerable hours of our own time, frequently spending the entire night nursing a static firing or launching through some stubborn problem. The regular work week at Peenemünde had been 48 hours: eight-and-one-half hours a day Monday through Friday, and five-and-one-half on Saturday. Officially, the work week was now 54 hours. Seventy hours a week was commonplace. We were paid straight overtime, but money was not the incentive. With strict rationing, money meant little. Rather it was the realization that the job was critical to the war effort, and that a long working day was merely a nuisance compared to the hardships being endured by others.

Night work with rockets had an excitement all its own. I would usually start with a break at Fischer's cafeteria for a snack. On my return, most of the desks in the office area would be abandoned, except possibly for one or two small groups of engineers talking out problems of the moment. Their voices sounded unnaturally loud in the half empty building, and echoed after me as I walked down the corridor to the control center.

There, an operator might be leaning casually against his console, clearly ready for a conversation about the weather, the war, how mixed up everything was, and even about rockets. Red and green lights on his console blinked on and off. Occasionally he answered the intercom, flipped a switch, or confirmed his action.

"What's X-time?" I asked him.

"It's still standing. We seem to have a bad connection in the main distributor box, a cold solder spot, or something. We've tried simulated launch test three times but can't get beyond prestage. . . . Yes, Erich, start key is on test. . . . No, I haven't touched a thing. . . . Yes, 27 volts is okay." He waved his arm in the general direction of the intercom. "He's trying to track down the trouble. Unfortunately this one's highly temperamental."

Conversations to men linked with the intercom were always a little difficult. You never knew for sure whether they were talking to you or the invisible party on the other end of the line.

Outside in the arena, the static firing structure towered in the background, studded with bright lights. Mechanics clambered about, shadowed against the lights, their voices sharp and near in the crisp night air. Floodlights suspended from masts and cables danced in the sea breeze. Weird shadows danced grotesquely on the arena walls.

The missile loomed bigger than it was, more than ever resembling something out of science fiction rather than a working piece of hardware. My skin pricked in the chill air. *Frau im Mond* seemed so close—yet so far.

Hours passed. Several times for brief periods we thought we had the trouble isolated, but each test attempt failed in exactly the same manner as had all the ones before. Finally, after midnight, still no closer to a solution, we called it off.

One after another, the men trotted back to the control center to wash up and change clothes. I lingered for a moment watching as the lights blinked off, singly and in groups. The last man left the stand, and sauntered into the control center. As his humming faded, the rocket seemed to shed reality in the midnight stillness, a shadowy fantasy aimed up at the star-sprinkled sky and yellow moon. The only sounds were the gentle pounding of the sea in the distance and the rustling of the trees, swelling and dying with the breeze.

The sounds of the meeting breaking up snapped me back to attention. Schilling made a few final remarks, thanking everyone for their presentations, nodding to each of us as we rose. There was no visible or audible appreciation of our work, of the trials, heartbreaks, or successes. Here, the impossible had so long been the necessary, it had become a matter of course. And out of the waste, horror, and duress of a great conflict a great new technological age was emerging.

7

ROCKETS AWRY

Late in December, 1943, while the Russian winter offensives raged once again, four MW-Missiles arrived at Peenemünde, the very first of the A-4's made at the assembly plant at Niedersachswerfen. This plant was called simply *Mittelwerke,* Center Plant, thus indicating no particular location to an outsider. Eventually, I saw this gigantic underground factory. It was spectacular; designed to produce up to 900 V-2's per month. Two parallel tunnels, each half a mile long, had been driven into a mountain. At regular intervals, these tunnels were connected by cross-galleries, resulting in a ladderlike floor plan. The tunnels and galleries were a minimum of forty feet wide and nearly as high. At many points, however, these dimensions were considerably exceeded. The main assembly line was arranged along one of the tunnels, with sub-assemblies feeding in from the galleries, which in turn were fed from the second tunnel.

Director Alwin Sawatzki's modest office was located at approximately the center of the plant. His staff included old-timers in the field like Arthur Rudolf and Rudolf Nebel, other experienced specialists drawn from Peenemünde, men transferred from other industries, and a sprinkling of specialists from concentration camps.

With all their experience, it was impossible for the few real experts to be everywhere simultaneously while the line was being set up. Thus, for thorough evaluation and feedback of corrective information, the first twenty production missiles were shipped to

Peenemünde for proofing on Test Stand P-7. As production missiles were brought up to standard, fewer and fewer would be delivered to Peenemünde. By the end of 1944, this procedure ended; in all, some fifty production missiles were launched from P-7 and nearby P-10 during this time. In addition, numerous production-line missiles were reworked at Peenemünde for research and development purposes, and then launched under a "V" serial number, mixed with and indistinguishable from Peenemünde-produced missiles.

In the course of further development, military training and reliability testing, additional production missiles were launched near Peenemünde by an Army unit, using both railroad and mobile road launchers. Finally, many hundreds were launched by German Army units in the swamps of Poland, for training and as a part of a large-scale statistical flight and reliability evaluation.

The first four production units arrived at Peenemünde by rail; two missiles to every three cars, nose to nose at the center of the middle car. They were covered with tarpaulins, for security reasons as well as a protection against the weather.

As the first cars of the train were pushed into the big hangar, the entire test stand crew gathered to watch the unveiling. The excitement soon subsided when the tarpaulins were pulled back revealing only more "cucumbers."

I was then in charge of the central evaluation of production missiles. It was our job to find the faults and correct them before proceeding to the next stage in the evaluation. For each phase, a bulky trouble report was prepared and forwarded to the production plant by special messenger. While the contents of these trouble reports must have made some people mighty unhappy, this exhaustive analysis resulted in rapid improvement of production quality.

For a reason I have never discovered, the first production missile was Number 17,001. At war's end the assembly lines were turning out missiles in the 22,000 numbering block. Missile Number 17,003 was the first to pass the evaluation program. Both 17,001 and 17,002 fell behind because of serious defects. Even so, hundreds of leaks, broken struts, wrong connections, burnt solenoids, cracked seals, mismade parts, and other production errors were found and corrected on 17,003 before achieving a successful static firing. January 27, 1944 was set as launch date.

On the surface, there was no difference between this and the 46 preceding V-series launchings. The missile itself, waiting patiently on the launching table, looked exactly like its predecessors. But there was one big difference, unmeasurable except by actual testing: the experience and skill of those who had assembled it.

At any event, though we were ready for the launching, 17,003 itself wasn't. When the missile was erected on the launching table numerous additional weaknesses came to light in the engine, the guidance system, and the rudder drive. There was a sizeable flock of visitors from design, development, manufacturing, administrative, and military groups present for the big event, but these gradually thinned out as X-time continued to slip.

It was long after the early winter night had fallen before we coaxed launch preparations into the final phases. Von Braun himself was among the few top officials in the control center as the crew retreated from the launching pad. He had spent the waiting period in his office in *Haus 4*. When everything appeared set, we called him down.

Since my release from the BGS, I had met von Braun several times during test firings, in coordination meetings or with visitors in the test area. I was more impressed each time. This night, he was wearing the usual dark gray leather overcoat and a hat which looked as if it might have served to protect him since the explosions of the early A-1 models in 1932. He arrived with time to spare, and I engaged him in conversation in the office. We talked over a few facts and figures on the troubles with production missiles in general and today's problem-child in particular. Gradually the conversation shifted to more general subjects, future plans, red tape, and anecdotes out of the past and present.

Whether in casual conversation or in a formal meeting, he always spoke in tight, well-formulated sentences. Once in a while, a faint hissing overtone would creep into his pronunciation. As a matter of fact, his use of bold Gothic letters in his handwriting just about perfectly reflected his manner of speaking. Later, I was to see this unusual clarity demonstrated in the ease with which he could produce a speech. His command of language as an instrument of communication was like that of a skilled lawyer. He was also a tactful, attentive listener. He would face you with his broad chin thrust slightly forward, occasionally interjecting a pointed question or a comment, the sort of remark that could come only from thorough familiarity with the topic.

He knew most of the people on the stand by name and was invariably friendly, positive, and understanding. When he had to overcome somebody's resistance to an idea or plan he would move close to his opponent, possibly grasp his lapel, and talk rapidly, with a most winning smile and flashing blue eyes, nodding his head and repeating quickly, "Nicht wahr? Nicht wahr?" It required more than average strength of character to maintain one's own view in these situations. But I cannot recall ever having seen him excited, shouting, angry, or testy.

This was the first long talk I had had with him. He had an excellent memory for essential technical detail. His approach to a problem, however slight, was always realistic. Obviously, he had substantial diplomatic abilities, which helped him further in getting his ideas across. He used the first person pronoun sparingly, and always gave credit where due in a convincing, pleasant manner. There definitely was the feeling of belonging to the team when you were in his presence. It was during that conversation that I realized fully why his reputation through the rank and file of Peenemünde engineers was so great.

The first warning siren interrupted us. Von Braun took a position at one of the periscopes; somebody handed him a headset. Ignition and pre-stage went off like clockwork.

"Main stage!" came the command.

The inferno of 250 pounds of liquid oxygen and alcohol burning every second smashed over the launching table. Out of the great ball of brilliant fire and swirling smoke, the missile slowly rose. I watched breathlessly as it began to leave the floodlit circle.

Suddenly I tensed. In a split second the jet faltered, and crept back into the nozzle and died. The rocket seemed to hang in the air, only its tail still illuminated by the floodlights. Then it settled back, touched the table and, in horribly slow motion, collapsed a little and began to topple. It struck the ground with a crash. The cylindrical tank section flattened. A moment of silence, and then, in quick succession, a preliminary explosion, followed by a thunderous detonation that jolted the control center violently. I staggered under the impact. A blinding flash of light swept across the arena, and in its wake, a tide of flames burst out from the launching pad.

This took just three seconds. For a moment, we were too stunned even to react. Muenz recovered first:

"Only firefighters immediately on station," he shouted into the intercom. "All other personnel stay in the control center until all clear." We would have to wait for the propellants to be completely consumed. The high-strength hydrogen peroxide was most dangerous.

I watched the firefighters move into action. A great hubbub, meanwhile, had begun in the control center. A guidance engineer and a powerplant engineer were in a heated discussion, the beginning of which had been lost in the temporary commotion caused by the departure of the fire crew. There seemed to be some idea that an erroneous emergency radio cutoff signal had caused the malfunction. The guidance engineer kept shouting that some switch had been tripped by the console operator. The latter was an elderly man whom I knew to be extremely reliable. Obviously still under the shock of the catastrophe, he was unable to speak a coherent sentence in his own defense. I moved to interpose.

All this time von Braun had not moved from his periscope. Now, he put down his headset and stepped over. In the background, Muenz was still busy with instructions, messages for headquarters, and answering questions over the intercom, all in his calm, steady voice. Von Braun likewise appeared unaffected, a little solemn, perhaps, but entirely collected. His voice was just a trifle louder than usual when he cut into the argument.

"This missile will never fly again," he said firmly, and the effect was complete. The argument stopped, and except for Muenz' intercom comments, the room became quiet.

"That's an obvious fact. We didn't accomplish what we hoped we would. But since it has happened this way, it is extremely important that we obtain every bit of information as to the cause of the failure. And by all means, let's not conduct a fault-finding investigation. No one is going to be hung. If a human error occurred with this experienced crew, it can only mean that our control equipment has to be made more foolproof." He smiled. "Don't forget, we have to place these monsters in the hands of Army units within a few months."

There was relieved laughter. The tension subsided, and the man at the console was able to tell his story. No manual cutoff had been given. He had merely moved his hand to the side of the console, following the main stage command, when, as far as he was concerned the launching procedure was over. Although the evidence was gone forever, some internal malfunction must have caused the disaster. A chattering relay, a bad solder connection undetected in checkout, a pneumatic line breaking under vibration—the possibilities were infinite.

As soon as the all clear sounded, we went out to have a look. Firemen were still flushing the ground and the twisted remains of 17,003. A strange smell which reminded me of gooseberry jam filled the air. The damage to our ground equipment was surprisingly small. The launch table was ruined, to be sure, though still recognizable. Sections of the rocket's skin and tank walls were strewn all over the arena. The turbopump had melted into a glob. The combustion chamber was only nicked, but enough to make it useless. The protective launch preparation housing was badly damaged, the windows gone and several boards torn loose. We also found damage in the underground relay and distribution cubicle, where burning propellants had seeped in around its heavy lid.

When this sort of thing happens, there is only one thing to do. Clean up the mess. Within two days, another launching was in preparation, almost as if nothing had happened.

"It sure would be nice if we knew what happened to 17,003," Muenz said to Hartmut the next day, somewhat ruefully. "But I'm afraid the war will be over by the time we have a decent telemetering system."

He had touched upon a sore spot. The powerplant people were extremely anxious to obtain information on their baby's behavior in flight. Sure, there were boxes and boxes full of records from static firings. But what about free-flight conditions? The influence of acceleration? Was the vibration pattern in free flight identical to that in tie-down tests? What about the influence of lower air densities at high altitudes? These were questions which needed answering and which remained undeterminable.

For quite some time, a telemetering transmitter called *Messina* had been under development by BSM. Its progress, for unknown reasons, had been very slow. Instead of being a useful tool, the device was hardly more than a passenger, and mostly an airsick one at that. With a telemeter on board only once in a while, and with a large number of them failing, the yield of useful data was rather limited. On top of that, guidance information claimed most of the transmission channels.

"We just blew up a million marks," said Hartmut, "in order to guess what could have been reported accurately by a tool probably worth the price of a small motorcycle." He had summed up in a nutshell one major problem which we never cracked at Peenemünde.

"I don't like this quietness," remarked Hartmut one day. "I think we're fooling ourselves if we assume they won't come again. Our camouflage can't work forever—not with all the activity that's been going on around here."

I had to agree. We had been stung once. An air of intense expectancy prevailed. The bombers would certainly be back.

"Besides," he continued glumly, "who knows when an A-4 will drop on the control center?"

We had discussed this possibility on many occasions. The control room, which served as a shelter during air raid warnings, had a roof of three-foot-thick reinforced concrete—thick, but not enough to take a direct hit from bombs such as they had dropped on Peenemünde before. Hartmut was determined to get better protection for P-7.

Maybe he knew what he was getting into; maybe he didn't. But it wasn't until months, numerous trips, letters, and conferences later that he began to make any progress: first in the form of shrapnel ditches. Eight of these, 100 feet long and deep enough so that, with dirt piled on both sides, a man standing upright could be concealed, were constructed in the woods immediately south of the big hangar. A light roof provided protection from the weather.

But this didn't satisfy Hartmut. He renewed his efforts to get the control center reinforced—receiving only half-hearted support from superiors in his own department. At last in June, husky 10-inch I-beam girders and pillars were installed to support the ceiling in both the control center and the instrument room. Simultaneously, an eight-foot thick covering of dirt was put on the flat roof, designed to detonate any bombs that might hit as far from the concrete itself as possible.

Meanwhile, large-scale production of missiles was really getting underway. At the same time, general preparations for military application gathered momentum. Two basic methods for launching were considered: from a massive fixed base on the coast of France, and from mobile launchers. Against the advice and counsel of those more closely associated with the A-4 effort, Hitler insisted on the former approach. Heavy concrete bunkers were actually put under construction at Watten, near Calais, under the code name *Kraftwerk Nordwest*—Powerplant Northwest. This approach, however, was abandoned when, on August 27, 1943, Allied planes dropped bombs into the still-wet cement. The mess that then solidified was beyond description.

Major attention then turned to mobile launchers—either road or rail. In addition, a study by the military under the code name *Regenwurm*—Earthworm—proposed tunnels in suitable mountains, out of which launching units would dash, launch and retreat. Experience soon demonstrated the tactical superiority of the road approach. Missiles could be launched from woods with just enough clearance to permit ascent of the rocket without touching any heavy branches. A road surface, hard dry ground, a rock, or a log bed would support the missile and launching table. Control consoles could be placed in flat ditches 200 to 300 feet away. It was fortunate that the foresight of the V-2 developers limited its dimensions to those that would permit its transport over the European highway system.

Operational V-2's used this method almost exclusively. A battery would be set up in a forest or at a street crossing, launch its missile, and then be gone within 30 minutes. Allied air superiority in late 1944 and early 1945, when these military launchings took place, was complete. Yet, I do not know of a single case where a military missile-launching site was detected and attacked by Allied aircraft, in a total of over 4,000 launchings.

Making the V-2 operational on a large scale required experts, and there was no source but Peenemünde. Increasingly, we would find familiar faces missing—reassigned to *Mittelwerke* to help iron out a mass production problem, or to Poland to assist in the training launchings. Eventually something like fifteen or twenty per cent of our technical people were taken this way. But they were partly replaced, at least insofar as numbers of bodies were concerned, by the "narrow-gage" military officer, a specialist in the new field of rocketry assigned to Peenemünde for training. These specialists-to-be could be distinguished from regular line officers by their slender shoulder epaulets—hence the nickname.

While we at P-7 were not directly involved with the military preparations, they did influence our activities, mostly in the form of increasingly frequent and often arrogant visitors. Such a group would alight from chauffeur-driven cars, stretch, flex their knees, and stalk around knowingly and expectantly. I was frequently dispatched to intercept the unannounced ones. It gave me great pleasure, being fully protected by the regulations and my civilian clothes. I could afford to be polite but stubborn.

"Pardon, sir, but this is a restricted area. May I see your clearance?"

"I am Colonel von Ahe. We wish to see the test area." The officer would look at me, slightly indignant, and start to walk toward the entrance. Casually closing the door, I would tell him:

"Awfully sorry, sir, but no one by that name has been announced by our headquarters. If you'll kindly wait outside, I will inquire immediately." All of which, of course, was the truth.

I would then go inside and call the Plant Protection Office in *Haus-4*.

"Say, we've got a bunch of colonels here . . . von Ahe or somebody. Know anything about them?"

"Let me check. Just a minute," would come the voice at the

other end. After a moment: "Yes, they checked in all right." He rustled some papers. "Purpose of visit: Discussion with Ground Support Equipment Section. How did they get there?"

"I don't know," I'd say, annoyed. "At any rate, I'll send them back to you. You fix it."

Conveying my utmost regret, I would send them packing back to *Haus-4*. "Army regulations, I'm sure you understand. We're anxious to show you around, but we have been called on the carpet several times recently. Extremely sorry, sir."

A good deal more indignant, the officers would turn back toward their cars, as drivers would dash out, doors fly open, heels click, and they would climb in and drive off like so many before them. Usually, they never came back.

This type of visitor caused unending delays and inconvenience. Their often-arrogant attitude did not ease the situation, either. The entire problem was the topic of many a debate in the office. That we would and should have visitors was generally recognized. In fact, we all felt a certain pride in being able to put on a good show—particularly if someone really important were announced. Basically, of course, our satisfaction was in being able to show what had been accomplished, to indicate what remained to be done, and thus gain support for our work. Frequently we were given an advanced briefing on such visitors: their importance, what they were in charge of, how far we should go in gearing the test activity to their visit. Men influential in budgets and supply priorities came first, and ordnance people a close second.

What we had to show impressed everyone. Demonstrations generating much fire, smoke, and thunder—above all, the launchings conducted with near-military precision by a highly skilled crew—may have given a premature notion about the project's state of development. However, this worked out for the best. For Germany, the war was going badly, and dwindling resources were increasingly available only to those projects that promised a quick return. To get more money we had to claim only a minimum of problems remained.

In all fairness, there were a substantial number of high-ranking

visitors—civilian as well as military—who displayed a surprising
amount of insight and understanding. These men took the time to
look around the control room and to examine test equipment.
And, most important of all, they asked questions. These were in
sharp contrast to those who waited out the countdown in the
Officers' Club; had their adjutants call in every few minutes about
the delay; usually arrived at the stand primed with anger and alcohol; and rode off with scant appreciation of what they had
seen. I will always remember one missile which we launched without replacing certain malfunctioning accessories because a general refused to wait any longer.

March 17, 1944 was a typically pleasant pre-spring day. Production Missile 17047 was set up in the arena and launch preparation was nearing completion. The first warning sounded before
noon. I had decided to watch this one from outside. I picked a
spot along the perimeter of P-10 where fifty-gallon drums with
fog generator nozzles attached (part of our scanty air raid defense system) were lined up at intervals. I pulled myself up on
one of the drums. Ahead, over the trees, the tip of Missile 17047
was just barely visible. The air was cool, fresh, and salty; the sun,
warm. The working platforms of P-1 were crowded with specta-
tors. A large crowd of soldier-trainees waited expectantly along
the shallow dune that separated P-1 from the road to P-10. The
eternal rustling of the nearby reeds had a soporific effect. My mind
wasn't really on the launching.

After a while, the final siren sounded; then the greenish trail
of the smoke bomb. Clouds of dust were stirred up inside the
wall and once again, as I had seen it so many times before, the
missile rose slowly into full view. It was a successful start. It
seemed, I thought lazily, that the production plant had cleared up
quite a few weak spots. Checkouts and test preparations of late
had hardly taken longer than with our development hardware.
Fifteen missiles had been launched during recent weeks without
a major mishap, half of them production models.

The rocket had reached an altitude of about 600 feet and was
starting its programmed tilt. I noticed, without really caring, that
I was sitting exactly in the line of flight. The roar of the engine
washed over me, and my hat nearly fell off as I leaned back to

watch. It is always difficult to determine the exact position of a rocket in flight. Above a certain altitude it always appears to be right overhead.

Suddenly at an altitude of about one thousand feet, the fiery jet disappeared, and a moment later there was dead silence. I watched it coast another few hundred feet. With the program started, it would return to earth in a narrow loop.

In my direction!

My daydream exploded like a balloon. I leaped to my feet and cut out towards the sea. In that same split second I saw the hundred-odd soldiers on the dune turn and disappear like dust blown from a shelf. Directly under the missile, a man was running frantically toward a reinforced concrete relay box cubicle.

I am always impressed, in circumstances such as this, with the number of things one can do and see in a few seconds. One of my first thoughts had been that obviously the missile could not be expected to stay up there forever. I began to run without really calculating my retreat. Instinctively, after covering perhaps 200 feet in what I am sure was world record time, I threw myself to the ground, my face toward the rocket. In these few seconds, 17047 had flipped over, tip down, and was rushing downward like a giant bomb. There was no other sound but the whistling hiss of that huge projectile. An instant later, the A-4 struck. It pierced the soft ground, and then there was an ear-shattering explosion. The blinding flash dazzled me for a moment, but I felt no shock, no pressure wave. In the same instant, I saw something that made me scramble back to my feet and try to put as much distance as I could between myself and the point of impact. The explosion had hurled into the air a shower—tons!—of fill dirt and rocky debris, scattering it in every direction. Another 100 feet, and I had reached an area where the fallout ceased. Then there was silence—and time for me to think.

All the while, I had really not felt any fear or concern; there just hadn't been time. It was actually a good hour before I suddenly felt some shock—tiredness in my legs, a great need to sit down.

But right then curiosity prevailed. I got to my feet and ran back. I found a giant crater, about 35 feet in diameter and nearly

as deep. It had already started to fill with ground water. A few
missile parts were visible; the familiar egg-shaped peroxide con-
tainer, the combustion chamber, badly smashed, and a few twisted
fuel lines. I caught again that peculiar smell of gooseberry jam.
The depth and shape of the crater told me why I had not felt
any pressure wave. The energy of the explosion had been directed upward.

I was joined by the man I had seen running across the field.
It was one of our photographers; he had found shelter inside
the relay cubicle. A minute later, panting, Muenz and the crew
arrived on the scene. They stopped and gazed in awe into the
crater. Then they saw us standing on the opposite side.

"How did you get here so fast?" exclaimed Muenz.

"Oh, I happened to be here when it came down," I remarked
as casually as possible.

Muenz stared at me.

"Well, by all means, tell us what it's like to dodge a rocket!"

This was only the first of many times I had to recount those
critical seconds to a fascinated audience.

One day late in April, 1944, just as I was entering a meeting
at *Haus-4* called to resolve some production testing difficulties,
von Braun stopped me:

"I'd like to talk to you after," he said smiling. "Come up to
my office, eh?"

When I arrived at his office about an hour later, Schilling and
Steinhoff were already waiting. Von Braun came to the point immediately.

"The Manufacturing Department is swamped by urgent—and
always more urgent—requests from various groups for experimental component installations for the missiles. Some of these are
compatible; some aren't. Manufacturing has no way of knowing
this, nor any way of evaluating the relative urgency of these requests. We need a coordinating group." He leaned forward. "You
have a good over-all knowledge of the basic systems, now, and
of what these problems can mean on the test stand. You've gotten the production missile evaluation program going well. Would
you be interested in setting up this office?"

"Yes," I said without hesitation. "It sounds interesting."

The problem was not new to me. It had been troubling not only the assembly people, but frequently those of us at P-7 as well: missiles arrived with installations which precluded others we intended to make while the missile was actually on the stand. Also, we were forever receiving last-minute requests for the addition of equipment which voided, to a large degree, the purpose of previously installed items. All this served to make various groups extremely unhappy. Such requests were often couched in references to the highest levels of authority, or hinted at the immediate collapse of the whole project or even loss of the war should they not be promptly fulfilled. And there certainly wasn't time to verify all these claims.

"I've already talked it over with Schilling and Steinhoff here, and Rees also," von Braun continued, leaning back in his chair. "You will be in an office with Mr. Kuers of Manufacturing Scheduling—just the two of you. We'll give you a three-digit group number and the necessary authority to make the thing work. After that, you're on your own."

Within a few days, the new office was set up in *Haus-4*. Werner Kuers, whom I had met on numerous occasions before, was an amiable, competent man who helped to make the project an extremely smooth operation.

We set up a large wall board, subdivided into areas indicating the principal stations of a missile in its life cycle: assembly building, P-7 hangar, firing stand, launch pad. We used metal tags to represent each missile, carrying its number, and the type of critical experimental installations. All existing requests for special devices were worked into the missiles under construction or in existence. Overflow was assigned to proposed subsequent production missiles. New requests were similarly handled. Thus, we were able to assure compatible installations. "Orphans," devices which otherwise might never have been tested in the proper relationship to other components, could be placed, and what we caustically called "brainstorms" could be eliminated with impunity.

Within a few weeks, we had freed ten missiles for additional uses. Millions of marks, or what really counted, tens of thousands of man-hours were saved, and experimental programs which had been sorely delayed moved forward smoothly. The freeing of a single missile would have more than rewarded our efforts.

At the end of May another change occurred. Unexpectedly, Hartmut was transferred to a military organization which was conducting launchings from railroad launchers. I was asked to take over for him on P-7.

P-7 was in high gear by now, a daily average of two static firings having been a long-established fact. In addition, there was a launching almost every day, and sometimes two. Stand P-10, meanwhile, had been equipped with a simple log-cabin-type control room and the basic necessary equipment, thereby making it an almost entirely independent facility. Upon Hartmut's insistence, balconies had been added to the servicing stalls of the big hangar, making a total of nine such working positions available.

On June 13, 1944, just a few days after D-day when the Allies launched their massive invasion of the French Coast, and I had been in charge of P-7 only a short time, we launched Missile V-89. It was a special test in at least one respect. It carried guidance elements of the ground controlled anti-aircraft rocket *Wasserfall*. This missile, also under development at Peenemünde, had a thrust of 17,000 pounds, and was to be controlled manually from the ground by means of a joystick control device. BSM had decided to test the response of this system on an A-4 in actual flight in order to determine the influence of the rocket jet on the guidance radio signal. We were told that the device would have no noticeable effect on the test in general. The ground controller appeared to have no trouble maneuvering the A-4, until it disappeared in a high cloud layer and he lost sight of it. As far as we could determine at that time, the flight was entirely successful and trouble-free.

What we learned a few days later, however, made us change our minds and view with even greater apprehension the now-almost-daily air raid warnings. Word came that V-89 had impacted in southern Sweden. The rocket, it turned out, had exploded in an air burst several thousand feet above the ground. This, combined with the fact that it carried the alien guidance system made it unlikely that anyone could use the wreckage to readily construct a duplicate or quickly develop countermeasures. But it could readily be determined that the intruder was indeed a large, long distance bombardment rocket. To this extent the cat was out of the bag.

8

BRENNSCHLUSS

Tuesday, July 18, 1944, was a bright summer morning on which we hoped to get another missile out to the pad and launched. I was just checking out the details when Muenz came tramping into the office. I looked up; he was agitated.

"We just received a full warning," he said. "I've already stopped all activities. Most of the men are on their way to the shrapnel ditches."

I looked at my watch.

"Kind of early, isn't it? Well, let the rest come into the control center. Keep telephone contact with the warning center. They're probably after Stettin again," I remarked, not really believing the last part. I kept thinking of the missile that had landed in Sweden, and how much, by now, the Allies must know of our activities.

"Maybe it's one of those reconnaissance planes," said Muenz after a while. "I hope we get the all clear soon; we're already late."

Interruptions like this were becoming more and more frequent. A single plane somewhere in the neighborhood could halt the entire operation for hours.

Half an hour, an hour, an hour and a half went by, accompanied by reports of planes moving in the periphery of our warning area. Then suddenly the tenor of the information changed.

"Enemy planes approaching our immediate area, extreme caution advised."

We all moved into the reinforced control room and into the

recorder room, closing the steel doors. More for the sake of passing time than anything else, I looked through a periscope.

"They're dropping leaflets!" I shouted.

Through the magnifying periscope I could see a shower of white papers raining into the arena. Some of them passed close by the scope. I could read the headline in bold letters: *Deutsche Arbeiter* —"German Workers." They later proved to be rather naive exhortations to quit and lay down our arms.

There was very little conversation. Then, faintly, we heard the sound of anti-aircraft guns. Once in a while a strange rustling or whistling noise was audible through the little ventilation hole between control room and tunnel. But no detonations followed.

I had just taken another look through the periscope when there was a tremendous explosion; the lights blinked out; and the world seemed to cave in. The thought flashed through my mind: this is the end. I was completely stunned, and in the darkness, lost all sense of reality. I remember a great amount of choking dust and noise; then silence, and the smell of burnt powder. After what seemed an eternity, someone opened the door to the front corridor. A few courageous souls carefully advanced to the outer door. There was no sound of planes.

Still hesitant, I moved out with the others into the dazzling sunlight. The engineers from the neighboring instrument room joined us. Everybody looked shaken, powdered white with plaster, hair unruly.

"Someone call the center. Maybe we shouldn't venture out too far yet. Everyone else stay here," I cautioned.

Surprisingly, telephone contact with the center was still intact.

"Enemy planes flying out of our area; no new approaches reported."

I nodded.

"Okay, let's have a look around. Feed your reports back to the office. And be careful. Mr. Melchior, could you round up some lights?"

Several men climbed the earthen wall; two or three others walked around it. About then the first people from the shrapnel ditches arrived, looking no less rattled than we. They had had close impacts, but no one seemed to have been hurt.

"I got a look into the hangar," one man informed me. "There was at least one hit there. One of the cranes is down. Looks like a mess inside."

Reports dribbled in: Pump house roof almost completely collapsed . . . damage to cooling pumps looks bad . . . no lights . . . danger of collapsing structures . . . control room suffered several hits . . . dirt covering blown off . . . concrete cracked . . . several periscopes damaged . . . number of hits in the arena . . . practically all boards and windows blown off launch preparation house . . . framework still standing, however . . . flame deflector undamaged . . . direct hit on one of the static firing towers, beyond repair . . .

So the reports came, adding up to a grim picture. I was afraid to think what closer inspection might reveal in this complicated maze of cables, lines, wires, and miscellaneous equipment. We feared that this working place of which we were all so proud might have been put out of business forever. Melchior returned with lights and we re-entered the control center. The office was in almost normal condition, though most of the window panes had been shattered, and papers were strewn everywhere.

At first glance, the control room looked unharmed. Then we saw that the lower portion of one of the periscopes had plummeted down from the ceiling and shattered a control console. The heavy metal section weighed at least five hundred pounds. It was the same periscope I had been using just before the bomb struck. Lucky, I thought, it could have hit me. *Or had it?* For the first time I felt a sharp pain in my right forearm; it had been completely suppressed by the excitement of the last half hour. I tried to lift the arm. I couldn't. The periscope had hit me! Now, the pain really became acute. I hooked my thumb into a coat buttonhole, which helped a little.

Then I realized that everyone had halted and was staring up at the ceiling. I looked up, and what I saw made me turn pale. Near the broken periscope, the ten-inch I-beam was bent several inches out of line. A supporting column had been violently twisted. What unbelievable forces had raged a few feet above our heads! Hartmut's name was mentioned numerous times that day.

Many of us owed our lives to his untiring efforts to reinforce the control center.

Within the next two hours, the picture of destruction was completed. The cooling water pump house was lost; the pump housings had been cracked and pierced by shrapnel. The battery room was a confused mess of broken glass and smelled of spilled acid. The hangar was badly damaged; there was a big hole in the roof, and one of the cranes was completely ruined. However, after the debris had been cleared away, we would manage with the one remaining crane. Happily, damage to the cable installations was far less severe than we feared at first. The lines to the arena launching pad all seemed to be intact; only the lines to P-10 were interrupted by a direct hit.

The over-all pattern of the attack now became clear. Thirty four-engine American bombers had dropped a carpet of 1,000-pound bombs which might have obliterated the entire installation but for the fact that the trigger had been pulled just a second or so too late. As a result, P-7 was caught only in the fringe of the carpet. The majority of the bombs had fallen in the woods immediately behind P-7, or into the area of the shrapnel ditches. We found it hard to believe that not a single man had been so much as scratched. There, the ground was literally studded with bomb craters. In fact, I was the only one from all of P-7 who had been hurt. Before the day was over, my broken right arm was in a cast.

Our survey assured us that we would be able to resume launchings at both P-7 and P-10. Reconstruction work started immediately, and less than two weeks later we successfully launched Missile V-205. Work inside the hangar smoothed out gradually. Steps were initiated to get around the loss of the pump house, by substituting a pressurized water system using high-pressure bottles manifolded together and pressurized with nitrogen gas (by-product of the oxygen generating plants).

Elsewhere around Peenemünde the production calibration firing stand near *Werke Süd,* P-11, was a complete loss. All told, 50 people had died in the raid, including anti-aircraft soldiers.

Even before the raid, there had been rumors that the Peenemünde Development Plant might become a private concern. Each new input set off vigorous discussions. The consensus was that this rumor was too good to be true. Those still in uniform shook their heads wearily.

"Don't believe it. We've been disappointed too often."

However, the unbelievable did become reality. On August 1, 1944, all supervisory personnel were called to a brief meeting in the Officers' Club. There, Paul Storch, temporarily transferred from the Siemens Company, was introduced as the new general manager of the development plant. He explained the new organization.

Henceforth, the plant would be known as *Elektromechanische Werke, Karlshagen, Pommern*—"Electromechanical Industries, Karlshagen, Pomerania." The company would operate, but not own or administer the installations in existence. Maintenance, transportation, and security would remain in the hands of the military organization under a Colonel Kamenitzky. Technical organization was left essentially untouched.

Although manufacturing, test, and administration were no longer under von Braun, the actual conduct of business during the remaining months of Peenemünde's existence did not reflect this change. Storch was an unknown quantity to everyone, and our product was unfamiliar to him. So must have been the standard operating procedures at Peenemünde. There was evidence he would not personally have chosen this job. However, my own observations made me feel that Storch accomplished his assignment with tact, restraint, and diplomacy.

The top layer of the new organization probably filtered out some of the coarsest military absurdities to which we were subjected. For the vast majority of the employees, however, the situation was completely unchanged. The company remained Government-owned; the facilities were still administered by a military organization; the VKN continued to exist; and military offices of a most confusing interrelationship continued to feed directions into the weapons program.

A major change was the reassignment of General Dr. Walter Dornberger, away from Ordnance and into the military application organization. For many years Dornberger had headed the

Army Ordnance Department in charge of rocket affairs. As *Chef Wa Pruef 11*—"Chief Ordnance Department 11—he had directed the section known as *Wa Pruef 11/V,* which was Peenemünde. Other activities of Department 11 included solid propellant development, as opposed to our liquid propellant operation, and the planning program for A-4 mass production. This latter was under the direction of Counselor Schubert.

Dornberger had been active in solid propellant rocket work as early as 1930. Under his patronage and against countless obstacles liquid propellant work in Germany eventually received official recognition. Dornberger was not only a soldier; his background included a complete engineering education, and his technical work had resulted in an honorary doctorate from the Technical University in Berlin.

Up to the time of his reassignment I had never met Dornberger. Old-timers often referred to him as *Seppl,* a good-natured nickname referring to the Bavarian-style leather shorts—*Seppl-Hosen* —which he sometimes wore when off duty. In those early days at Peenemünde, Dornberger had been a familiar and respected figure at the plant. Many of the leading engineers there had known him since the early thirties, from the days when the nucleus of the group was forming at Kummersdorf near Berlin. In 1937, most of these people transferred to Peenemünde, for which ground had been broken in August, 1936 after a joint Army-Air Force *Übereinkommen,* a mutually advantageous agreement, had been reached to build the facility. During the years of construction, activation, and early A-4 development, *Seppl* had spent much of his time there.

I envied those who had had the opportunity of participating in these early activities. The Oie launchings especially must have been interesting and exciting. The Greifswalder Oie, usually just called Oie, is a small island six miles off the Baltic coast near Peenemünde. Less than a square mile in area, its only inhabitants had been the lighthouse crew. While the main plant on Usedom was still under construction, Oie proved to be an excellent experimental launching station for the A-5, smaller work-horse forerunner of the A-4. Powered by a 3,330-pound-thrust, pressure-fed engine, the A-5 was used to carry guidance equipment aloft for study and development. Two parachutes, ejected at the A-5's several-mile-high apex, would gently return the missile to the surface of the sea, often in good enough condition for servicing and reuse.

The objectives of these launchings required that they be performed on clear days only. That meant waiting periods of days or even weeks, and long, long idle evenings in the modest quarters which were provided. This led to development of a closely-knit professional community life, surely a primary contributing factor in the later character of Peenemünde itself.

As the tasks of his office mushroomed, Dornberger's visits to Peenemünde had necessarily become briefer and less frequent. As the importance of Peenemünde grew in the military mind, his arrivals were more and more often in the company of generals and other officers and officials that periodically descended on P-7.

But now simultaneously with his reassignment, liquid propellant activity was separated from his department and set up as a distinct entity called *Wa Pruef 10* with headquarters actually in the Peenemünde military headquarters building. While these measures seemed a logical result of our growth, other organizations were at the same time being created by the Army Logistics Department, the Army Ordnance Office, by SS chiefs and party bosses, by government agencies and industrial associations; and a maze of subdivisions, main offices, suboffices, commissions, subcommissions, committees, subcommittees, special committees, task forces, review boards, resulted. It was hard to say which were reasonable and which were utter waste and duplication.

I suppose it all must be regarded as the primary curse of success. Rockets, so long objects of scorn and skepticism by high Nazi officials, including Hitler himself, were now "the miracle weapon" that would change the tide of the war. They were fashionable and we began to know it. We got the priorities we needed, but we also got meddling interference and an unprecedented degree of "organization." Like an A-4 itself after *brennschluss,* at engine cutoff, the concept of the secret weapon was moving on its own momentum.

That night in the darkness of my blacked out room I listened to the restless drone of bombers heading down Berlin-alley. I

shuddered for Irmel. I had not heard from her for several days—
the mails were becoming infrequent and unreliable—and had not
seen her for several weeks. In my early days at Peenemünde,
when the train connections to Berlin were still good, we saw each
other nearly every week end, meeting usually in Ahlbeck, near
Swinemünde, where we spent many pleasant hours on the beach.
I thought with a smile and feeling of warmth of the time she spent
there mending my socks . . . and the excellent cakes she brought
with her each time. But now these trips were hardly safe, or possible. In semi-drowsiness my thoughts wandered again to the
plans we had made so many times for after the war. After the
war? Sickeningly, I wondered if there would be an "after the war"
for us. If only she had left Berlin as so often I had urged her to
do. When sleep finally claimed my consciousness, the throbbing
drone of the bombers continued to bore its way into my subcon-
scious. It was one of many restless nights.

9

PEENEMÜNDE AT WAR

The tortured I-beam and the cracked ceiling in the control room were constant reminders now that Peenemünde was a target for Allied bombers. There were two questions in everyone's mind: Will they come back again?; and its inevitable counterpart, will that ceiling survive another direct hit?

Nobody believed we would escape further attacks or that much strength remained in the ceiling. And there certainly wasn't any chance of getting it repaired. Despite our priorities and popularity in high places, by now there were scarcely enough materials on hand to keep the basic program going—much less divert resources to such things as bomb shelters. It was a problem we had to solve ourselves and was a source of frequent discussion.

"That ceiling won't survive another raid," I remarked one afternoon, shaking my head. It had been said many times before, and no one argued.

"But where can we go?" protested one of our engineers, raising his hands in a gesture of hopelessness. "We've got fifteen minutes after a warning to find shelter, and no transportation other than our feet."

He had hit on one of our most critical shortages, transportation. Any place we decided on as a shelter in future raids would have to be within walking—or running—distance. As the discussion continued, I had the sinking feeling that already Peenemünde was beginning to die. True, we were launching rockets with gratifying frequency, and malfunctions were occurring less and less.

But other than rockets from *Mittelwerke,* critical materials for those we built ourselves, food, and the unending influx of visitors, it seemed as though shipments into Peenemünde had all but died out. What we had, we had. That was it. If something wore out or was bombed out, we improvised. If that was destroyed, we did without.

"What about the reeds along the shore? Certainly they won't bomb those," someone ventured.

"Not intentionally," I replied, shaking my head. "But if they come in from that direction and start the carpet a little early . . ."

And so the discussions went. The trees toward *Werk West* wouldn't be much better for the same reason. Without motorized transportation the shelters around *Haus-4* were too far away, and besides, they were probably already fully assigned. Then someone suggested a relatively new shelter near *Werk West*. It was much too far by road, but through the woods, he contended, it should be only a ten-minute walk. I sent him and another on a trial run of it. They were gone for two hours.

"We got lost, and it is a little farther than we thought. But," they explained, "we can still make it in fifteen minutes' walking."

Fifteen minutes can be a long time, particularly when you realize that you don't just up and leave an operating test center. There are things to be closed down and turned off, things that take time. However, we had no better alternative, and, I rationalized, if the bombs did start impacting before we reached the shelter, the woods would offer some protection at least. Then I thought of the two hours they had been gone.

"But how can we be sure of finding the shelter in a hurry?" I asked. "We'd better mark the trail. Mr. Kaschig, please arrange for some simple sheet metal strips, or something of the sort, with which we can mark the trees. And, we'd better get started right away."

By evening of the following day we had marked the first third of the trail. We intended to finish the job next morning, Friday, August 4. But like all other work at the station, that work was interrupted by a pre-warning, followed shortly by a full warning.

Within minutes we were on our way following the markers. We did not go in one large body, but rather were strung out along the way. I was in a group of five or six people. Others were ahead, out of sight, more were behind. Some had decided to sit it out in the woods. Others had gone down to the shore.

Soon our metal markers ran out. We continued, following a barely discernible path along a clearing covered with weeds, grass, and underbrush. Other than our own self-noise and the gentle rustling of the breeze, there was a pristine silence. The August sun was hot; the soft sea breeze, refreshingly cool. To find this wilderness so close to an ultramodern installation surprised me. But for the sense of urgency I would have thoroughly enjoyed the walk. Then the path ran out. Ahead of us lay a dense stand of timber. There was no trace of a trail nor any evidence that man had ever before entered this forest. We stopped for a moment, shrugged, and plodded straight ahead into the woods. It was dark and cool, the sun filtered into bright fingerlets by the roof of tall firs. Here and there giant beeches and massive oaks elbowed their way up through the conifers. We seemed to walk interminably with no sign of either shelter or highway. In fact, when we paused to listen, other than the soft breathing of the woods itself, there was no sound whatsoever. I was getting nervous.

"This is as safe as anywhere," remarked one of our party. "Let's stop and relax."

"All right," I nodded. "If we don't see anything within the next five minutes, we do as you say. *Einverstanden?*"

We started forward again, our "fifteen minutes" long since consumed. Distantly I heard the hum of planes. Then it faded. And began again. The five minutes were just about gone when, quite unexpectedly, a huge block of concrete, almost lost in camouflage, loomed up through the trees just ahead. We couldn't have hit it more directly if we had had markers all the way.

The general atmosphere was relaxed. From various directions, mainly along the highway, people were streaming into the shelter. A number of people loitering near the open entrance were smoking, which was prohibited inside, or just chatting. A little farther away, noticeably isolated, a group of thirty or forty concentration camp prisoners were sitting on the ground, watched by a couple of bored guards. I couldn't help noticing the difference between these poor souls and the only other group I had run across, during my days at Siemens in 1938. Concentration camp prisoners carried colored markers on their arms to indicate the type of offense. Six years earlier most of these I had seen were murderers, thieves, sex offenders, and the like, with only a small proportion of political prisoners. Now, I noticed a shocking predominance of black political arm marks. What had started out as a means of getting able-bodied prisoners to do useful work had apparently turned into a device for political persecution. A feeling of uneasiness came over me . . .

"*Achtung!* Everybody in the shelter. Enemy aircraft heading toward Peenemünde."

I went into the shelter. I noticed that the prisoners preceded us and were herded into a reserved area. Once everyone was inside, the heavy steel doors clanged shut. A warden urged us to move to the upper levels. It was a fairly well equipped building: many simple benches, sanitary facilities, and ventilating systems.

Several of us from P-7 gathered in an upper-story room. I looked around: what a familiar sight! How many hundreds of times I had been caught away from home during raids during those days in Berlin. If I happened to be walking in the streets, I would take to the nearest public shelter; if I were riding the U-Bahn, I usually remained stranded at one of the stations until the all clear was sounded. Sometimes this meant many hours of waiting, so I had always carried a book with me to read.

But wherever it was, in the subway station, in a regular shelter, or here in Peenemünde, it was always the same. Cold unscreened lights, uncomfortable benches, barren concrete walls. Depending on the location, the time of day, even the season, the population of the shelter might vary. Sometimes I had found myself in groups trapped on the way home from work, tired, sleepy, close-mouthed people; other times, particularly on Saturday evenings in the theatre and restaurant areas, I was part of a noisy, gay, apparently unconcerned crowd. During daytime raids, I would be surrounded by business talk spiced with frequent references to lost time and impatient glances at watches. But when the sound of nearby anti-aircraft fire came, or when rumbling bomb detonations made the shelter shake and sway, the universal character of all bomb shelters superseded the temporal differences of its occupants. Stiffened backs, stern faces, staring apprehensive eyes, alarmed women pulling their frightened offspring close, the children asking unanswerable questions.

For myself, the worst thing about those minutes and hours was the realization that there was nothing whatsoever I could do except wait and hope for the best. But instinct was there, struggling with this feeling, making me wish I could do something, defend myself in some way—fire a gun, throw something, anything!

A distant roar brought me back to 1944.

"The carpet," half a dozen voices hissed.

They were after Peenemünde again! That rolling thunder removed all doubts. The whole event called a "bomb carpet" probably lasts no longer than a few seconds, but somehow I imagined I could almost count the number of impacts: something like the sound magnified a thousand times of the contents of a crate of rotten oranges being emptied onto a wooden floor. All talking ceased, and the inevitable character of the bomb shelter, the character of fear and helplessness, set in. The reverberations recurred several times, at intervals of minutes. Then all was quiet again.

Soon the shelter doors were opened, and we hurried back over the now-familiar trail. I was tense with expectancy. What had happened to our precious facilities? Around the shelter and all through the woods, there was nothing to indicate there had been an attack.

Then I caught sight of the big hangar. I felt a twinge of horror. All the windows were gone; the big door was wrecked; and it looked like damage had been done to the office and laboratory wings. Those of our people who had hidden close by were already at P-7, busily fighting a few small fires when I arrived. One, who had watched the raid from a nearby one-man concrete pillbox, chattered nervously, assuring me over and over that he would never stay so close again.

Fewer bombs had been dropped this time, but with devastating accuracy. The still-unfinished pressure system which we had improvised to provide coolant water during static firings had been blown to pieces. Only one of the movable structures was intact.

As I surveyed the damage, Willi Muenz came over to my side. "Well," he remarked, "you know what this means."

I nodded grimly. This clearly meant the end to any static firings on P-7. Even launching operations would be handicapped by damage to cables and lines. Repair work in the hangar would create another bottleneck. But as before, reconditioning began immediately at a feverish rate.

Elsewhere, P-11 had gotten it again. The big hangars in *Werk Süd* had also been hit. Casualties were low: ten people dead, including anti-aircraft soldiers. This figure, we all agreed, reflected our increased alertness.

While the repair work was under way, I took a brief vacation to give my broken arm a chance to heal completely. Thus, I was absent when the fourth and final raid took place, on August 25, 1944. It was a daylight raid, and I watched it from Koserow— one of the most excruciating experiences I have ever endured.

When the planes had at last completed their work of destruction and headed homeward, I hurried back to Peenemünde. Because of disrupted transportation, the trip took several hours. An almost familiar scene unfolded before my eyes. It was hard to tell the exact extent of new hits, but certainly previous damage had been aggravated and much repair work voided. Once again, our people set out to rebuild, mend, jury-rig, and patch. But material was scarce, and transportation was difficult all over Germany. Our repair effort went much more slowly as a result. Still, it was only six weeks before launchings were once again successfully resumed at P-7.

Although we could not know it then, there were to be no further raids on Peenemünde.

10

THE PERSONALITY
OF PEENEMÜNDE

We had just finished a meeting in von Braun's large paneled office in *Haus-4* concerned with the recent air raid on Peenemünde and the resulting cessation of static firings on Test Stand P-7. I had picked up my papers and was about to leave when von Braun spoke:

"Mr. Huzel, would you wait a moment, please?"

He closed the door and motioned me to be seated. Only he and his younger brother Magnus, his technical staff assistant, remained in the room. He sat down, paused, looked questioningly at Magnus, and then turned his attention toward me:

"As you may be aware, we are having difficulties at *Mittelwerke* in several critical areas. The inferior quality of certain components is seriously reducing output. We are just going to have to divert more people to get the program out of trouble."

He paused again, got up, and gazed out the window, obviously thinking. I knew about *Mittelwerke,* of course, and its troubles, and had a pretty good idea of what the huge subterranean factory was like, although I had not yet seen it. It was located at the foot of the Harz Mountains, amid great scenic splendor; but if this were leading up to an offer to transfer there, I certainly wasn't excited by the prospect. Von Braun turned away from the window and sat on the edge of his desk. He leaned forward, and it was clear that he had made, or reaffirmed, his decision.

"We've decided to send Magnus there to take over gyroscope production. Would you be interested in taking his place as my technical assistant?"

I was completely surprised, and definitely interested. I made this clear immediately. To work closely with Wernher von Braun was an exciting prospect. I was to make the change as soon as I could familiarize my successor at P-7 with his new job. We discussed the various problems involved in my transfer, and about an hour later I left, elated. That night Hartmut and I celebrated my good fortune.

Dr. Kurt Debus succeeded me at P-7, and for several days I was rushing back and forth between *Haus-4* and P-7. Debus was ideally suited for the post: capable, energetic, and with considerable experience as engineer in charge of the guidance effort in connection with static firings and launchings. His contact with the mechanical aspects of our work was extensive, and he had contributed much to test stand activity planning. The fact that P-7 had been hit so severely in the last raid was unfortunate, for it would limit the usefulness of this very able man.

The response of the entire test stand personnel, from test crew to mechanics, to the need for rapidly refurbishing P-7 had been heart-warming. Support shops gave us delivery promises of a few days which, amazingly enough, were generally fulfilled. Such *esprit de corps* and determination made my departure from P-7 a sad one.

My duties with von Braun ranged widely, from classifying all and actually handling much of his correspondence, to setting up meetings, untangling snags in plant operation, opening up bottlenecks, chasing up scarce material, sorting out personnel problems, and smoothing over political (and technical) difficulties that were bound to arise in such an intensive and complex organization. My new job brought me in contact with everyone in the plant, and, as it turned out, my experience on P-7 proved invaluable, for it had given me an intimate working knowledge of many of the things in which I now got involved administratively.

Once in my new position, I arranged a trip for myself to Bavaria where many of my things—namely clothing—had been put in storage when I was drafted into the Army. Casual clothes around a test stand were not only permitted but recommended. In my new position, however, I needed suits; and since rationing didn't allow their purchase new, I had to retrieve those I left behind.

This trip was a revelation. In the isolation of Peenemünde, I had not realized the extent of damage from Allied air attack. Practically every city or town of any size I passed through showed the marks of heavy bombings, particularly in the immediate vicinity of railroad stations and along the tracks. Trains were scarce, severely overcrowded, and a mixture of very old and deteriorating new cars. Hotel accommodations along the way were inferior, and the food was poor. People looked haggard and dispirited.

By contrast, the remote little Bavarian village of Oberstaufen where my friends lived was reminiscent of the romantic charm of that wonderful book *Heidi*. The walk up from the station carried me along a winding footpath through green and flower-studded meadows, a scene of perfect peace and natural beauty utterly removed from the harsh reality of war. The sight of the three-story chalet with its three balconies running all around the house and its typical flat angled Bavarian roof made me grateful for this opportunity for a brief escape from the world without. Lounge chairs and a brightly colored umbrella completed the setting.

The enchantment of the moment, however, vanished when I learned that my friends' son-in-law had just been reported killed in action. I stayed only a short while and in a few days was back in Peenemünde. I wrote Irmel of the sadness in all that beauty, as much to relieve the ache in my soul as anything.

Magnus' office on the north side of that wing of *Haus-4* was extremely simple, though large. Severely damaged by fire during the big raid, repairs had been held to the barest essentials. The walls were unpainted plaster; there was no carpeting, and little furniture. Later, after Magnus had left, I hung some pictures which helped a little. One day Magnus and I were going over von Braun's correspondence together. The door was closed so that we could work undisturbed. His secretary, Fräulein Beise, acted as watchdog. The date was September 8, 1944. We had reached the bottom of the stack of letters and memoranda, were leaning back, relaxed, and discussing some of the less formalized aspects of the job. Suddenly, the door burst open, and Fräulein Beise stood there, a newspaper in her hands.

"I'm sorry, Herr von Braun, but . . . look!" She held the paper so that we could read the headlines.

Vergeltunswaffe-2 Gegen London im Einsatz, it declared—"The V-2 in Action Against London."

Magnus and I rose quickly and hurried across the hall into his brother's office. The news had arrived there also, and the room was rapidly filling as staff engineers drifted in. A dozen excited conversations were going at once. Von Braun cut in on the enthusiasm with a note of sober reality. This was not the final payoff—far from it. The V-2 was not yet fully developed. Many specific problems remained to be overcome, despite the exaggerated propaganda of the Hitler government. Propaganda inevitably begins somewhat in advance of cold fact, but it is nevertheless essential that the propagandists themselves be aware of the real situation. We had considerable doubt on this score. We feared Josef Goebbels and his people believed what they were saying about the V-2: repeated references to the *Wunderwaffen* —"Miracle Weapons"—and Goebbels' remark, since become legend, made to General Friebe less than a week earlier: "General, if the German people only knew how close we are to final victory!" Von Braun was realistic:

"Let's not forget," he addressed the excited group in his office, "that this is only the beginning of a new era, the era of rocket-powered flight. It seems that this is another demonstration of the sad fact that so often important new developments get nowhere until they are first applied as weapons."

I was acutely aware, and I am sure most of the others were also, of the care with which von Braun had selected his words. He had recently suffered an official denunciation by SS informers whom Himmler had sent into this area, based on the allegation that he had been sabotaging the war effort to "fantastic space-flight projects." He had been quoted out of context at a social gathering at Zinnowitz. Nevertheless, he and two others were moved under guard to Stettin and placed "under restraint," and possibly only avoided prosecution through the stern intervention of General Walter Dornberger. The accusation, of course, was utterly ridiculous. The rocket in World War II enjoyed a position in history comparable to that of the airplane in World War I— and look what happened to aviation in the "first fifty years of flight." All of us held the dream and the conviction that this work would one day lead to space flight. I have always been convinced that von Braun's arrest was more a tactic in Himmler's power play to take over Peenemünde (which he eventually did) than based on any suspected disloyalty on the part of von Braun and the others.

More and more, as time went on, I began to realize that virtually everything I did was dictated, in part at least, by shortages: of manpower, of equipment, of time. It was rather like trying to put together a jigsaw puzzle with a constantly diminishing number of pieces. Transportation problems took a lot of my time: every day brought a raft of requests, denials, justifications, explanations. Somebody needed more ration stamps: there were charges of unauthorized use of a vehicle; actual cases and false charges of black-marketeering with government property; and so on and on and on. A constant problem was the release of rocket propellant alcohol for stretching limited gasoline supplies, a blend, incidentally, which worked quite well.

Two serious problems developed with respect to the technical drawings—blueprints—as it were, which represented and detailed the results of all our efforts. Throughout all the birth pangs of setting up mass production and future modifications of the V-2 at *Mittelwerke,* we always kept a complete set of up-to-date drawings at Peenemünde. These had to be protected at all cost against sabotage, theft, or enemy action. Since the recent raids, the design section had been evacuated to Koelpinsee, farther south on the island. There was the simple matter of getting guards for the vault where the drawings were kept. Twice I had called a Major Heigel on this matter.

"I'll do what I can," he replied for the second time.

I shook my head. These were signs of incipient breakdown.

The other problem was one simply of drawing maintenance. Many of the design group had necessarily been transferred to *Mittelwerke.* These transfers often involved equipment as well as men; including even printing machines. Our resources were dwindling, irreplaceably so. Yet the work load kept increasing. Surely, I reasoned, this cannot continue forever.

Still, everything I did and everything I attempted was thwarted by scarcity. There wasn't enough of anything, and more and more projects were not being carried to completion.

The mail from General Dornberger's office often told the story with frightening clarity. One letter, dated September 22, 1944, was particularly alarming. It concerned liquid oxygen supplies, and informed us that a major production plant in France would shortly fall into enemy hands. This, continued the letter, would leave seven plants available to us, capable of producing a total of about 200 metric tons of liquid oxygen a day. A detailed breakdown of the remaining plant locations and capacities was included. Considering losses sustained in storage and transit, and the need for developmental and production calibration, there would be enough liquid oxygen for approximately 25 operational launchings a day, and virtually nothing for our developmental effort at Peenemünde. Worse, all the plants above ground, except one, had been bombed at least once. Von Braun had three "in" boxes on his desk, graded according to the extent to which correspondence did or did not require his personal attention. Dornberger's letter would go in box number one.

Some of the problems which came up seemed almost trivial by comparison with the circumstances in which we increasingly found ourselves. Of course, they weren't trivial, particularly to those responsible. But many actions and procedures that are necessary and/or desirable in normal times diminish in importance and become trivia, or simply become futile in the face of disaster and dissolution. The sense of depression and inevitability of an Allied victory that I brought back with me from my trip to Bavaria was not helped by the increasingly severe shortages that plagued us—mute evidence of the slow and relentless incapacitation of German industry. Scarcity underscored the sense of urgency that by then pervaded every corner of Peenemünde, and increasing urgency, in turn, only served to emphasize the mounting totals of what we did not have and could not get.

As a result, the normal, everyday type of problem that fell

within my administrative responsibilities, when it came up and
when I had time to attend to it, served almost as a moment of
relaxation from the dire and seemingly insurmountable tasks that
were increasing with each day that passed.

I had just finished reading the discouraging letter from Dornberger when the buzzer sounded.

"Yes?"

"Mr. Schaeffer of Personnel is here, Mr. Huzel."

"Send him in."

Schaefer came in tapping and fumbling in every pocket. I don't
smoke, and this was a hint for one of my meager ration of cigarettes. I laughed and handed him one. He was an amiable, good-
humored, talkative man—usually well up on the latest rumors.
For so young a man he was startlingly bald, which gained him
the nickname around the plant of Platten-Schaefer—"Skin-Head
Schaefer". He sat down, leaned back and savored the smoke. He
had troubles.

"There's been a recommendation for decorating twenty people
here at Peenemünde, and I haven't been able to get any action
at all on it from higher up." He inhaled the smoke deeply. Then,
he scowled. "But worse than that, I've got to get together a list
of men to be released from military deferment. Miserable."

He was sincere. He did not like the job of selecting men to
go off and die over others who would stay on here in the relative
safety of the plant.

"Not a thing I can do, either. Orders straight from Berlin. An
emergency measure . . ."

Again, shortage breeding urgency, and urgency breeding shortage. More men were needed at the front. More men were needed
at Peenemünde. More men were needed for German industry, on
the railroads, on disrupted telephone lines, on farms, everywhere.
And the supply of men, like that of everything else, was constantly
dwindling. I could not get excited about Schaefer's problem with
the decorations. On the other hand, I did not envy him the job
of deciding who would be sent to the front, or who would stay
behind. I could not help him on either score. Suddenly, we heard
a loud rasping voice beyond the door.

"It's him again," muttered Schaefer. "Nimwegen!"

Part of the personality that was Peenemünde, Nimwegen was a puzzle to almost everybody. He had appeared as if from nowhere one day: a big, heavy, corpulent man who had operated a hotel in the area at one time and had somehow gotten a position in the car pool. His talent for organizing (in the sense of the GI slang term, "liberate") had become legendary around the plant —but always for the benefit of the plant, never for personal gain. He was a "big time operator," *par excellence,* blessed with irrepressible savoir-faire. It was no trick, for example, for him to call the Admiral of the Navy installation at Swinemünde and identify himself as speaking for the *Reichsführer SS* (Himmler), and then follow through with requests for materials, food, fuel—almost invariably with success.

He was, nevertheless, a loudmouth and coarse in his manner, and often his methods skirted close to the edge of the law. All of these things tended to isolate him from the rest of us. In a way, this was a shame, for on numerous occasions he was a big help to the plant, and later on he demonstrated great, unselfish courage by making sorties via truck into the eastern combat areas, collecting pigs and other domestic animals abandoned by the fleeing population—all right under the noses of the advancing Russians. And though we could not know it then, he was later to play an important role in the relocation of the entire Peenemünde effort to Bleicherode, in the Harz mountains.

In these days, two vastly different personalities ran Peenemünde. Paul Storch from Siemens in over-all charge of the plant, and Wernher von Braun. Von Braun is one of those personalities who radiates energy and enthusiasm, and who speaks and acts with authority—the kind of authority that comes only with complete knowledge and understanding. Von Braun was young, dynamic, and convincing.

Storch was a man of about 55 years of age, graying but well preserved, his round, healthy-looking face punctuated by a mustache. He dressed with restraint and taste. He spoke with a slow, subdued, but very determined voice. He was unused to being disputed or questioned, and when, in one of the many meetings he held, disturbances occurred while he was speaking, he would simply cease talking until there was silence. Where von Braun was direct and to the point, occasionally even blunt in his style of self-expression, Storch's manner was one of indirection: he would never say that someone should be fired, but rather that "to his sorrow it might become necessary to separate ourselves from" a man.

I had had even more time at Siemens than I had so far accumulated at Peenemünde. Thus, I watched with constant interest and amusement the rubbing together—it was never a blending—of these two cultures, Siemens and Peenemünde: the big business operation and the advanced engineering laboratory. I don't believe that Storch ever really understood what it was he was running, and feel that we must have been a continual source of amazement to him—not so much in what we did, but the manner and philosophy with which we did it. It came out repeatedly at his meetings.

These, he invariably conducted, or at least tried to, with great dignity and with the format and diction becoming a top executive of a company approaching its hundredth anniversary—a good five times the age of the infant industry of rocketry!

On a typical day, Storch opened the discussion with a few general announcements. Then he shifted to the problem of destroying our classified material as rapidly as possible in the event of a surprise enemy attack. To this end, plant chemists had developed a concoction which when poured on paper would dissolve it. There was a need to equip existing vaults with the necessary plumbing and triggering systems. Also, we needed more vaults. All classified material was to be deposited in these vaults every evening.

"Since we thoroughly settled this matter at our previous meeting," said Storch, "we can now turn to the question of how we shall actually determine what we mean by 'classified material,' particularly in regard to this problem of speedy destruction. I am sure you all agree that it would be very desirable if we could reduce to some extent the amount of paper which your employees must carry to the vaults every night. I suggest that . . ."

"Pardon me, sir, for interrupting you," cut in Dr. Ernst Steinhoff, clearing his throat. "But there are a few circumstances I thought I should mention at this point."

Storch, with a dignified movement, took down his reading glasses, leaned back in his chair, and looked at the speaker, benevolently and with just a trace of tolerant incredulity that he might have overlooked something. He had been reading his presentation and had not noticed that Steinhoff had been growing increasingly restless and had several times started to interrupt before finally getting impatient enough to actually do so. Steinhoff appeared very young; he might have been mistaken as a university senior in fact. He had tenacity and drive, and no patience whatsoever with "diplomacy." Although the underlying cause for this was his obstinate honesty, it could be awkward.

"I talked this business over with my people," he continued bluntly, "but they don't want to carry out the plan as we discussed it."

Storch looked at Steinhoff as if he were some strange new creature. His lower jaw dropped ever so slightly. He looked baffled, almost rattled, and certainly incredulous.

"Did you say that *you,* their *director, you* explained these measures to your employees, and they *refused* to do it?"

There was probably no single case of this type in his personal association of many years with the Siemens Company—or at least none that had ever penetrated to his level. The situation was deteriorating. Then, Mr. Rees, Director of Manufacturing, spoke up:

"We are having similar problems to those of Dr. Steinhoff. We think we've got the answer. I suggest Dr. Steinhoff and I get together later today."

Rees always said the right thing at the right time. He seldom spoke up, but when he did, his remarks were clear, concise, and convincing. He had certainly saved a delicate situation here.

This incident serves to highlight the kind of personality problems that arose from time to time, particularly after Peenemünde became a private enterprise and Siemens came in to provide business management. As a result, by tacit agreement we all strove to keep incipient problems out of the Storch meetings, unless circumstances forced them into the open. It was von Braun's expressed desire that the new organization work without friction; that special requests from Storch's office be given prompt and effective attention. As a matter of fact, Storch interfered relatively little with our regular operating procedures.

There were many kinds of meetings at Peenemünde: the Storch meetings; the so-often futile gatherings originating in the offices of the more politically minded; hard factual, problem-solving meetings of the front-line technical groups, and finally the smooth and effective pooling of mental effort conducted by von Braun. It was these meetings that I found most useful and most stimulating.

Von Braun took his work in big gulps. Meetings were comparatively few, but when they occurred, they covered a lot of ground. Von Braun didn't conduct a meeting, he led it with perception and incisiveness. He knew most problems at first hand, and those few that he didn't, he knew by instinct bred of long, intimate and successful experience in the field. He repeatedly demonstrated his ability to go coherently and directly to the core of a problem or situation, and usually when he got there and it was clarified to all present, he had the solution already in mind —a solution which almost invariably received the wholehearted support of those present. It has been suggested from time to time by people who have had only casual contact with him or simply know him by reputation that von Braun is a politician (nothing else!), a top technical brain, a diplomat, or "just an able administrator." At Peenemünde and since, in this country, he has demonstrated that he is all of these things, as the demands of the moment require. But above all, he is a leader: not through demagoguery, but through courage, dedication, enthusiasm, brilliance of mind, wisdom of experience, and coherence of expression.

Von Braun may have driven his people hard at times, but no harder than and often not as hard as he drove himself. There were jobs to be done and just so much time and material with which to do them. As time got shorter and materials scarcer, and as demands from the high command came simultaneously for greater range, greater payloads, greater accuracy, we applied ourselves all the harder, improvising as it were on improvisations. We learned then that a new age is not born; it's built. And to us, after all, had fallen the task of laying the foundation.

In 1942 I was a graduate—and experienced—electrical engineer who had been drafted after the first German setback in Russia. Here, as a private, I learn to drive a truck. A far cry from rocketry! I'm the one with the glasses looking at the camera.

These bachelor quarters were typical of those at Peenemünde. Each had 40 rooms, and there were usually two men to a room. All rooms had central heating and running water.

Central Telemeter Building (BSM) after the first successful Allied bombing raid on the German missile center. Portions of this building were later restored to usefulness.

"Blockhouses" in the days of Peenemünde were less gaudy and more elementary than those at today's rocket installations. Note the schematic layout of fluid flow lines.

(Left), a plumber's nightmare: the working innards of a V-2 liquid rocket engine were complex, but precisely made, undergoing terrific stress during operation. This maze of pipes, tubes, gas generator, turbo-pumps, etc., gives no hint of the basic simplicity of this propulsion concept, so much more efficiently utilized in today's liquid rocket engines. (Right), V-2 missile undergoing preliminary test and checkout prior to tanking, countdown and launch.

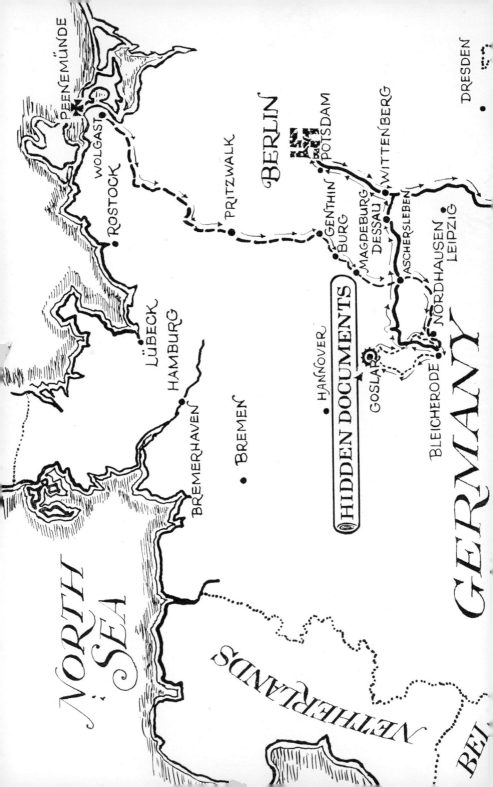

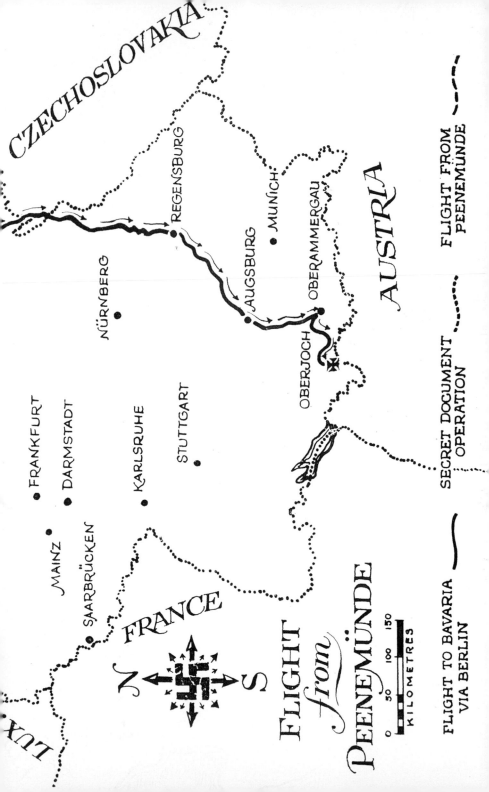

CZECHOSLOVAKIA

AUSTRIA

REGENSBURG

NÜRNBERG

AUGSBURG

MUNICH

OBERAMMERGAU

OBERJOCH

FRANKFURT

DARMSTADT

KARLSRUHE

STUTTGART

MAINZ

SAARBRÜCKEN

FRANCE

LUX

N

S

FLIGHT *from*
PEENEMÜNDE

0   50   100   150
KILOMETRES

FLIGHT FROM
PEENEMÜNDE

SECRET DOCUMENT
OPERATION

FLIGHT TO BAVARIA
VIA BERLIN

V-2 mid-sections under construction. Longer tanks carried 150-proof alcohol; shorter ones to the rear, liquid oxygen. Sign reads: "No Smoking."

Machine shop section of the Components Manufacturing Shop could have been almost any machine shop in any other plant in the world by its appearance. However, the high precision and quality control required for V-2 parts made it a very unusual shop indeed.

Static firing under way at Test Stand P-7. Note deflected rocket exhaust. Graphite vanes riding right in the flames move during flight to provide attitude control for the missile during the boost phase.

V-2 missile about to be launched, as seen from the general direction of the flame pit. "Prestage" fed by propellants under static head only, is already burning. Cable is still connected to missile instrument compartment. Now-disconnected box fill line is conspicuous from frosting. Note small flame deflector at bottom of launching table.

(Above), First successful launch of a U.S. Army Redstone missile at Cape Canaveral on the morning of August 20, 1953. As a project engineer on the Redstone rocket engine, I had come a long way from those days in the spring of 1942 when I was learning the intricacies of truck driving.

(Right), Explorer-I, America's first artificial satellite of the earth, used the Redstone missile as a first stage booster. This same missile later boosted America's first astronauts into non-orbital space flights.

11

DEATH OF PEENEMÜNDE

By now the military situation was changing rapidly. Russia was closing down on Germany from the east and the north. The Allies were closing the other half of the vise from the south and west, and in between the life blood of Germany was being squeezed out drop by drop. Everything we did, all our thoughts and actions, all our engineering effort, was influenced in one way or another by the rapidly changing military situation. The area under German control was steadily shrinking, and the mounting ferocity of Allied bombing was steadily disrupting and demolishing the means of manufacturing and transportation upon which our work depended. We were plagued on every hand by scarcities—scarcity of raw materials, scarcity of manufactured parts, and scarcity of what was now referred to in official speeches as *Menschenmaterial,* human material.

Meanwhile, Allied advances in France were pushing our launching batteries farther and farther north into Holland, farther and farther away from London. We were forced to investigate every possible means of gaining added range. Our current effort was to increase tank capacity, hence propellant supply and, in turn, rocket burning time. This involved considerations affecting the entire missile system, and made demands upon the talent and imagination of our engineering staff often greater than those of totally new designs. Not only were we seeking to fit a developmental product into mass production, but we were also trying to modify it without reducing the production rate. Two factors worked

127

against us: the pressure of time and the existence of established design limitations.

Along the way, we encountered a new and entirely unforeseen phenomenon we tagged as *Luftzerleger,* air or reentry bursts. Many of the missiles were not impacting in one piece but were breaking up before striking the target. During the time that we launched the A-4 out over the Baltic Sea we had never noticed this fact. The dye spot was always there in the water, and the fact that occasionally there were several spots in a large cluster we attributed to dispersion under water after impact.

But then we started conducting launchings with solid ground impact points, firing from the area of Blizna in southwestern Poland into the uninhabited Pripet Marsh region. We soon discovered the air burst phenomenon. The regularity with which impact was characterized by a shower of missile parts scattered over a large area, rather than by the familiar deep funnel, was disturbing, to say the least.

For better observation of the last seconds of the missile's trajectory, some of the experimental launchings were made straight up into the air from Oie Island. This gave the launching crew a weird feeling, but as planned, the earth's rotation inevitably resulted in a water impact or air burst a mile or so west of the island.

Some of these launchings took place shortly after sunset and provided a spectacular show as, at high altitude, the missile would rise out of the earth's shadow and suddenly light up like a brilliant, rapidly moving star. As it rose, its speed would slow until at peak trajectory it seemed to hang motionless for a moment before starting its earthward plunge, faster and faster until it was again swallowed up by the earth shadow. It was on one of these shots that a world altitude record of 117.44 miles was established with an A-4 and a burning time of 67 seconds.

But nothing conclusive was ever learned from these tests. On the other hand, evidence gathered over the months indicated that structural weathering of the forward portions of the missile skin, resulting from overheating, was the culprit. We were finally able to reduce this problem, though we never did eliminate it entirely.

All told there were 264 developmental A-4/V-2 launchings

during the life of Peenemünde starting on June 13, 1942 and terminating on February 19, 1945. Of these, 165 were launched from Test Stand P-7, 39 from Test Stand P-10, 23 vertical launchings from Oie, and 37 launchings from other locations such as Test Stand P-6 and Siedlung. Of these, 117 were production missiles made at *Mittelwerke,* two were Peenemünde-made A-4b's, and all the rest were A-4's produced right at Peenemünde. The breaking point in these launchings came in the spring of 1944 when the proportion of successes began to rise rapidly. Approximately 3,550 V-2 missiles were launched operationally, of which some 650 did not reach their target, owing primarily to air burst. The proportion of failures on the ascending side of the trajectory from these military launchings was four per cent, provided the missile had been stored properly and was launched within a few days of its manufacture. Since the number of launchings per month was only slightly less than the production rate, there was seldom much delay. Production at *Mittelwerke* from September 1944 through March 1945 averaged 650 per month. Based on a study of 1,200 V-2 launchings, an impact reliability of 78 per cent was established.

The explosive payload of the V-2 was always 2,200 pounds (one metric ton). Experimental rockets with extended propellant tanks achieved a maximum range of 298 miles, though the final effective range of the operational V-2 was 220 miles. In operational use, tanking time was reduced to twelve minutes. That the V-2 was developed into an almost "idiot-proof" operational weapon is attested to by the high reliability rate.

My new assignment on von Braun's staff brought considerable changes in my living habits—best summarized as "irregular hours." Many times I had to dash off to an emergency meeting in connection with the Heidelager launching program and the continuing study of the air burst problem; or I would find myself at Pudagla in Steinhoff's headquarters, sitting into the small hours of the morning in a technical meeting on gyroscopes; or another time I might spend most of the night at a conference on pressure regulator adjustments at *Ersalin–Ersatzeillager Lindenmayr,* the code name for the component laboratory.

It was not so much that my hours had been particularly regular at P-7, but there at least I was on familiar technical ground and P-7 was always in one spot. Now I got into technical area details which were new to me, and the locations of these meetings were widely scattered. The journey all the way home to Koserow on such nights grew tiresome; train connections were irregular at best, and it was a long walk from the station to my place. As a partial solution I took a room in the bachelors' quarters in *Haus-1,* just a few steps from *Haus-4.*

Living on the base, as it were, I had more opportunities to sit and chat with friends at the Officers' Club over dinner and after; or even just to relax and read. Movies in the big hall of the service building at Camp Karlshagen provided a welcome escape from reality. The films, fortunately, were usually unrelated to the war, and as often as not were old pictures, though almost invariably of good quality. It is strange, the things one clings to, to provide support in a precarious and deteriorating situation: usually things that are old and familiar and reminiscent of more stable, pleasanter times. Then, as often as not, we would be snapped back to reality as the image would flicker and the sound growl into silence. The hall would grow dark and a message would flash on the screen:

ENEMY BOMBERS ENTERING AREA

Occasionally we would manage to get over to Zinnowitz for an evening and a dinner reminiscent of happier days. This town had been a swank seaside resort, and a number of fine restaurants were still operating. My favorite was the *Preussenhof,* located right on the beach and overlooking the sea. There, the waiters wore white tie and tails; there were white tablecloths; and the food was pretty good for those times. Since meat was strictly rationed, any meat dish was quite small, but fish wasn't rationed, and this was a specialty of the house. As wine was unavailable, it was acceptable for the customer to bring his own—which we usually managed to do. After dinner the waiter would spend twice the time with the ration coupons that he did with the bill. These were moments of pleasure stolen out of tragedy, and our humor was always high as we finally made our way back to *Haus-1.*

I usually spent my weekends at my rented quarters in Koserow, where sometimes mail would be waiting for me from Irmel and my parents. I would spend my time there strolling along the coastal cliffs, writing letters, reading, and catching up on the news of what was happening to Germany, which became less and less encouraging with every week that passed. It was hard to extract the truth, of course. The papers contained only government approved releases, which were echoed by the radio. However, there was at least good music, and there were no commercials. We also encountered a very effective form of Russian propaganda. For example, a German announcer might say:

". . . and by the end of the day German forces had recaptured the villages lost during the preceding twenty-four hours."

Immediately another clearly audible voice, almost as though it were in the German studio, would cut in:

"All lies! The Russians have penetrated the entire front! Germans are on the run!"

Apparently the Russians had a powerful beamed transmitter and an announcer completely familiar with German and possessed of quick wit and intelligence. He would listen to the German newscast and immediately broadcast his comment back on the same wave length. There was never anything sophisticated about the interjections. It was simply the voice of doom. No promises of liberation were offered, only predictions of defeat, death, and destruction.

The German government countered this tactic by having the newscaster read his broadcast so fast there was no time for interjections. This was unpleasant to listen to, but effective, until the Russians began firing their vocal salvos in between pieces of music or during any other moment of silence. Eventually, a transmitter was set up which received, amplified and rebroadcast the Russian message, but phase-shifted half a wave length, thus canceling out their transmission.

However, we did not need the Russian propagandists to tell us what was happening. Deteriorating conditions were increasingly reflected in our daily life. We had become accustomed to the big shortages. But now little shortages began to get severe, things almost trivial against the broad backdrop of events but symptomatic in the extreme of the approaching end. Clothing ration was reduced to such ridiculous alternatives as one topcoat a year *or* a shirt and some underwear. Metal collar buttons, once lost, became virtually impossible to replace. There were no shoes whatsoever to be had, with or without ration coupons. Even repairs were virtually impossible, unless you were lucky enough to lay your hands on a piece of worn-out industrial drive belt and also able to find a cobbler. First, the big things disappeared. Now the little things were gone. Soon, everything would be finished. And with Germany, Peenemünde, too, would die. What will be the future of rocketry, of space flight, of trips to planets and distant stars? Who will pick up, I wondered, where we are forced to leave off?

For some time there had been rumors that the entire facility might have to be relocated. Now, they grew more persistent. The Russians had crossed the Vistula and were pouring over Poland. They'd soon be in East Prussia, then Pomerania. Clearly, some action regarding Peenemünde was necessary.

But for those of us who worked in Peenemünde, and were thus familiar with the project, the complexity of the program and the extent and type of facility necessary to continue such a development effort, it was difficult to imagine how such a relocation could possibly be accomplished. Thousands of employees and their families would have to be moved, as well as carloads of equipment and data—and all this in the presence of a disrupted railroad network, of extreme shortages of trucks and gasoline, and daily Allied air attacks.

The dilemma we faced was brought home to us with increasing sharpness as the days and weeks slipped by. One of the most frightening of all these reminders was the endless stream of fugitives from the invaded eastern provinces, who, since early in the year, had been passing through Usedom on their tragic flight from destruction and war. They moved west from East Prussia, from Pomerania, moving into the Oder district, where they were offered the dismal choice of crossing the river at Stettin or farther south, or of swinging north and west and using the ferry at Swinemünde. Those who made the latter choice continued on through Usedom and over the Wolgast Bridge into the rural province of Mecklenburg, literally going right by us. It was a sad and a terrifying sight. The line of march was marked by virtually all conceivable forms of the most primitive transport: horsecarts, pushcarts, wagons, all heavily loaded with household implements and bedding, and often topped with a tired and dirty child. The people walked wearily, with exhaustion, disbelief, defeat on their faces. Mostly they were old men, women, and children. From villagers and others who talked to them came unbelievable tales of Russian brutality—of pillaging, burning, wanton killing, and worst of all, of rape and murder of old women, mothers-to-be, and young girls. The tales of horror were as constant and unvarying as the unending stream of pitiful humanity.

We could not help, so we sought forgetfulness in our work. Here, on the surface at least, things seemed little changed. Progress continued toward something that we knew now would never be brought to fulfillment.

Many, in those troubled days, openly expressed the thought that it might be wise to separate themselves from Peenemünde. After all, they would say, the plant was now under the direct command of Himmler himself! Everyone captured alive was sure to be killed: "I heard so over the Russian radio station."

But we inevitably came to the same conclusion. We had no sensible choice but to continue working. We certainly were personally unable to change the tide of events, so the only thing we could do was stick to our job.

In any case, I began to gather my things, packing them in boxes and suitcases and transferring these to my room in *Haus 1*. When the time came for the move, as I now felt sure it soon would, I did not want to be bothered with personal preparations. Clearly, the plant would require my full time. I wrote Irmel and told her that I feared the end of my work was not far off.

On January 31, 1945, a cold and cloudy Wednesday, several of us—section chiefs, department directors, and von Braun's immediate circle—were called into the Professor's office. He stated the exact situation to us. There was grimness in his voice when he spoke.

"Kammler has just ordered the relocation of all the most important defense projects into central Germany," he said quietly. "This is an order, not a proposal."

He waited a moment for the reaction to run its course. When the murmuring and exclamations had ceased, he continued.

"We will probably be relocated to the area of Nordhausen, near *Mittelwerke*. It might be Frankenhausen, however, or perhaps both.

"We have the problems, first, of who will go, and second, in what order. Top priority must be assigned to those whose effort is required to maintain production at *Mittelwerke*. Second, those engaged in problems of increasing range and improving missile accuracy. Third, those who are working on the anti-aircraft rocket *Wasserfall*.

"Dr. Debus and the entire P-7 launching staff will remain here until further notice. This, incidentally, includes all those required for the assembly effort at *IW-Süd* of experimental missiles.

"Now, I will want an immediate analysis from all department directors telling me how many people you will be moving, and how much equipment.

"All vehicles must be checked and brought up to optimum operational efficiency. This will be Hueter's job. We'll want a complete inventory of our gasoline supply and our tire stock. These should be assigned proportionately. We will want a snowplow, too, Mr. Hueter; arrange that, please. Mr. Schaefer, you will be in charge of our efforts to reduce personnel rapidly. We want no more than one thousand people left here when the major move is completed."

"How about transportation to our new location?" I asked.

"This will be primarily by truck. We'll also have one railroad train at our disposal, pulled, I believe, by a diesel switch engine." He turned in his chair. "Mr. Nimwegen, I want you to direct all transportation affairs. To help you in this, I'm assigning to you Sergeant Koenig, three men, and a typist.

"Let me emphasize the necessity for haste in getting full reports on all these matters to me. I'll want them inside of two hours, and they must indicate exactly how many people you will be moving, how much loading space you will require, how much area you will need in the new location. Also, what you are completely abandoning."

Schaefer broke in.

"This will mean canceling a number of draft deferments, I presume."

Von Braun nodded. This was a sad and a futile thing, indeed, because to each of us in that room it was clear that further resistance and killing was useless.

"We'll need a list of all names and year of birth."

I was hardly back in my office before the flood of calls began. Everybody wanted help, or to be told where to get help: spare parts for trucks; which of the guidance projects were to be considered most important; travel authorizations, hysterical demands for more details. Late in the afternoon, of January 31, Nimwegen came hurrying into the office and excitedly declared that he needed an extra telephone. It took some talking, but I managed to arrange it.

All the while I was involved in an endless series of conferences with von Braun, sometimes just the two of us, sometimes in the company of department heads or section chiefs.

The New Year found fierce battles raging all along the eastern front, and the Western Allies were preparing their first thrusts across the Rhine. A great pincer was poised around Germany and was beginning to close. Within days, the first groups began to leave Peenemünde. The end was beginning.

During the late evening hours of February 2, while most of us were still awake and very busy, a message came in that the Russians were attacking Eberswalde, a medium-sized town located on the principal railroad between us and Berlin. Twenty-four hours later we knew this was just a vicious rumor, but it certainly produced results. Nobody wanted to be trapped, and that meant hurry!

By this time most of us had come to a definite conclusion. If the war were lost, if we were going to become prisoners of war, then let it be the Western powers, and not Russia, into whose hands we fell.

The last and biggest relocation meeting took place about eight o'clock on the morning of February 3, while the rumor of Eberswalde's fall still hung over our heads. Von Braun directed the discussion; in addition to himself, Riedel III, Schilling, Rees, Butt of the company railroad, Hueter, Schaefer, Debus, Reinke of

Supply, Nimwegen, and numerous administrative assistants from various departments were present. There were also military representatives.

The first big fact established was that all of us would go, not just part of the staff, as had been suggested at earlier meetings. "But we will go as an organization," von Braun stated firmly. "This is important. We will carry our administration and structure straight across Germany. This will not be a rout."

This was somewhat comforting. Von Braun turned to Schaefer. "You have the personnel tally ready?"

Schaefer nodded. The list he read was broken into six groupings:

A-4 Development and Modification: 1940 people
A-4b Development: 270 people
Wasserfall Development: 1220 people
Taifun Development: 135 people
Supporting Shops: 435 people
Administration: 325 people

"This makes a total of 4325 people," he concluded. "Of these, eighteen per cent are women. Thirty-eight hundred are located on Usedom, the rest are scattered in various assignments in outlying areas.

"However, it can be estimated that about thirty per cent of these will not be relocated." He shuffled through his notes. "Those not going, whose military classification is 1-A, will report to the local *Inselkommandant,* and those who are not covered by this will simply be released or reassigned to other war plants in this area."

Nimwegen reported briefly on the transport situation.

"Effective immediately, all railroad cars are being retained in the plant, and no empty cars are being returned to the Federal Railroad System. For the present, we must keep all motor vehicles here also, to be used as shuttles between the labs and shops and the rail sidings. No other trips will be permitted, except for the procurement of food."

The general problem of who actually would direct the physical relocation of the plant now came up for discussion. The experience of most of us with the military made for universal agreement on one point: the plant itself, through some emergency agency, should direct the operation. "Shut out the military entirely," growled someone. Rees interposed.

"This has a bad feature, though. It may deprive us of some of the necessary priorities. Also, don't you think the presence of the military will offer some protection against interference from various government agencies?"

As usual, Rees was succinct and to the point. The solution we finally adopted was to get Oberstleutnant Boergemann, an energetic officer of the *Wa Prüf 11* staff, to serve as chief transportation officer, and to have him appoint Nimwegen as his deputy.

Problem tumbled upon problem.

"But the available railroad cars alone will never be able to carry the entire load."

"True," agreed von Braun, "but we will also have some ships at our disposition—about ten large self-propelled punts, scattered in the harbor around Peenemünde, and probably as many barges. These can be towed to Lübeck, through the Trave-Elbe Canal, and then on to Schönebeck, near Magdeburg. Very close to our destination." He went to a map on the wall, and with his index finger jabbed out the route for us. "We also have hopes that the Navy at Swinemünde will loan us a 2000-ton vessel."

The meeting closed with three specific assignments. Butt and Reinke were put in charge of all railroad operations, Nimwegen in charge of truck movements, and Bernhard Tessmann in charge of ships.

We went to work with a vengeance. Virtually all the coordination came through von Braun's staff, and this kept us busy night and day. Such a simple thing as the procurement of boxes for packing was in itself a large task. Some of the technical sections needed hundreds of them. We devised a color-coding system for ready identification of each box upon arrival at our new headquarters: white for administration, green for design and development, blue for manufacturing, red for test, and so forth. All this time each department was frantically trying to determine which thirty per cent of their people were not to be taken along, and how many of the seventy per cent who were going had families, and how many people were in these families.

We cleaned out a lot of excess paper in that move, to be sure, because we destroyed everything which was not vital.

In the midst of this, we learned that the Russians were still a good deal farther off than had been reported. However, we did not slow down our preparations, because it was only a matter of days before what had for the moment proved false would become fact. The reduction in pressure did result in a little smoother operation, and some of the hysteria was gone. Importantly, we had acquired great momentum by that time. It is notable that through all of this, there was never any panic.

Late that evening, von Braun called me into his office and told me he was flying to the new location. He would survey the area, find out just what the authorities had in mind, and from this information, he could assign the various units to their new places. In his absence, preparations were to continue at the same pace.

Not long after von Braun had left, Rees began loading the first railroad cars. Next, we began to move the office furniture onto the barges.

The first train was to carry 525 people, employees and their families, plus a few loaded boxcars. Date of departure was to be February 17.

Nimwegen really proved his worth during those hectic days. He was all over the place, procuring blankets here, kerosene lamps there, gasoline, diesel oil, and a score of other hard-to-get items. He managed to collect no less than twenty complete field kitchens.

Methods? Well, we all looked the other way, counseling ourselves that the purpose justified the means. And events certainly proved Nimwegen's hard, realistic attitude to be perfectly correct. He had reached the conclusion that it was no longer a question of which German agency was going to use this material, but rather: was a German agency *or the approaching enemy* going to use it?

By this time, the SS was in almost complete control of Germany. In an effort to bolster the sagging military organization, they had set up road blocks and checking stations all over the country to intercept soldiers "looking for their units" in the wrong places, or civilians of younger vintage who looked like they might be AWOL. We considered that this powerful organization might well prove a stumbling block to our successful relocation.

Even this was not beyond the indefatigable Nimwegen. He simply invited the SS officer in charge of our area into his office for discussions, played his plenipotentiary game to the hilt, and just happened to have an attractive secretary and some bottles of port wine handy.

We utilized as much as possible the advantages accruing from the attachment of our weapon system to SS Chief Heinrich Himmler. Pompous passes and letterheads sprang into being conveying to all and sundry that we were a part of the SS organization. These naturally included reference to our association with Dornberger's agency, *BZBV Heer.* By a strange quirk of misunderstanding, some of this *BZBV* stationery emerged as *VZBV,* an utterly meaningless expression. Here again Nimwegen's preposterous talent turned the error to advantage. He made *VZBV* a top secret agency, not to be interfered with by anyone save Himmler himself. Soon *VZBV* signs began to appear in letters several feet high on boxes, trucks, and cars. Indeed, it provided complete protection against any interference; thus, despite the growing confusion inside Germany, all of our essential personnel and a good portion of our equipment did arrive at the new location.

Help came in many strange forms, too. The guidance group at Lubmin discovered that it had fifteen mules at its disposal, and these were put to work pulling heavily loaded carts. And one day, out of the mass of people fleeing westward, there arrived at Peenemünde a woman with a stable of some fifty select horses, raised by her in East Prussia. This woman had friends and relatives at Peenemünde, and her offering thus provided—literally—additional horsepower for transporting our equipment south.

On February 27, von Braun was back and immediately called a meeting in his office of all department and section heads, and their staff people. He explained to us the pattern of the new organization.

"What has been set up," he said, "is an *Entwicklungsgemeinschaft Mittelbau,* a sort of central cooperative development structure. We will be only one part of this organization, which will also include Henschel Aircraft, the Ruhr Steel Corporation, Aircraft Components, the Gyroscope Company, Dornier Aircraft, and *Walterwerke,* as well as a number of other smaller organizations."

Von Braun's function in the new organization was to act as over-all technical director, with the assistance of a planning staff.

"For our effort, several test areas will be established. There will be smaller areas set up for the X-4, X-7, *Taifun,* and *Schmetterling* missiles, and larger setups for the A-4 and the *Wasserfall.*"

We all looked at one another. Test stands for the A-4, just by snapping your fingers? This told us a sad story indeed! Von Braun ignored our expressions of disbelief. He always managed to hide his own feelings when to reveal them would only have damaged his cause. I was sure this was not his personal concept.

Names new to us were involved in the new group. There was a Dr. Konrad to act as coordinator for propulsion systems, and a General von Gyldenfeldt to head a *Luftwaffe* counterpart to Dornberger's *BZBV Heer,* the *BZBV Luft.*

Operations were to be centered around Bleicherode, a small cotton-mill town south of the Harz Mountains. Dornberger's headquarters would be in nearby Bad Sachsa, formerly a mineral resort. Locations had already been earmarked for many of our departments, places like Sangerhausen, Weissenborn, Artern, Gross Bodungen, among others.

"Launching from Peenemünde will definitely halt," von Braun added. "Dr. Debus, your mobile launching convoy will be formed and dispatched to the general area of Cuxhaven, in northwestern Germany."

Debus could not know it at the time, though we all might have suspected, that he would never fire any rockets from Cuxhaven, at least not under German auspices. Von Braun remained for a few days more at Peenemünde, clearing up a few last details, and then he was gone permanently. I am sure he must have had strange feelings as his plane took off; it was the last time he was ever to see this place into which he had put so much of his life.

We continued to load furniture on the barges, but I do not believe much of this ever arrived at its destination. Later, I heard stories of desks, drawing boards, chairs, cabinets, stranded on the banks of the Elbe near Magdeburg. Naturally, classified material was found in some of these desks, and this meant trouble for somebody. More trains, loaded with engineers and their families, and with heavily laden boxcars, pulled out. Gradually, Peenemünde grew very quiet, in strange and somber contrast to the years preceding.

My activities now revolved entirely around the relocation effort. I was the last remaining representative of von Braun's office, and soon messages began to come in from *Münchhausen,* which was the code name for the telephone exchange in the new area. It seemed that there were housing difficulties: while empty rooms were available, furniture was lacking. Shipping any from Peenemünde was now out of the question. In fact, we shortly stopped our attempts to ship the office furniture.

One of my continuing duties during these fading days at Peenemünde was the preparation of travel authorizations for convoy leaders and transport supervisors heading south, the men guiding our equipment and documents to the new location. These passes were essential if we were to avoid interference from the SS. Usually they ran something like this:

TRAVEL ORDERS

Mr. Hans Schulz has instructions to move to a classified dispersion location in central Germany, in accordance with official orders by *Reichsführer SS,* dated 11 February 1944, Reg. No. A-12110, concerning the relocation of installations of an importance decisive to the war. He is authorized to select any means of transportation necessary, and to perform acts otherwise in pursuit of this order. He is responsible for the complete transfer of all employees accompanying him, as identified by their plant identification cards. This move is subject to Top Secret handling.

This transfer order was received by radio and must be completed within five days. Mr. Schulz is authorized to use High Command telephone and teletype lines and is required to report immediately any delays in the completion of this assignment.

All authorities of the Army, SS, and civilian administration are hereby requested to give Mr. Schulz all possible assistance in the prompt execution of his assignment.

For the *Reichführer SS*

—and somebody's signature. It is a testimony to the state of internal organization, or lack thereof, in Germany at this time that such a document could in fact provide a man with free access to those things mentioned. It was a combination of desperation and fear of the SS.

The cafeterias were dismantled and shipped away, and with them, their personnel. Soon only a small contingent remained. At this point the quality of the food improved markedly; after all, there was no reason not to use what was left behind. Even alcoholic beverages reappeared, something which had previously been as scarce as cigarettes.

The atmosphere was strange indeed; a sort of suspension of reality seemed to have taken place. Movies were still shown at Karlshagen, and a few short trains moved between areas. One of the flak units, which included in its personnel a number of women telephone operators, sponsored a few dances. These usually ended early since the port wine was sweet and easy to take, and the girls were not used to it any more, and it made them sleepy.

The few remaining weekends at Peenemünde I spent at Koserow, more often than not, bicycling through the woods to Zinnowitz farther east. It made a pleasant trip, at a time when pleasures had suddenly become both simple and rare.

At Koserow, I ordinarily visited Hartmut's family, or just strolled along the beach, reading or watching the waves and the clouds. Once in a while there were visitors at my apartment, and we would make some music and have a few drinks. We even got so we could ignore the air raid sirens; after all, who in the world would bomb Koserow? During the week, when I was at the plant, I slept in my office; there was electricity there most of the time, unlike Koserow, and the furniture was reasonably comfortable.

The last days began to unwind from the dwindling spool. Hartmut and his family were now gone, relocated with his unit in Bad Sachsa. I completed my own plans, finished packing my essential possessions, not too many now, and eliminated everything else. I waited for instructions.

Subconsciously, I would listen for the distant growl of a test taking place at P-7, a sound that never came. The uneasy stillness of a death watch had settled over Peenemünde.

12

RELOCATION AND FLIGHT

I needed no special directive regarding my departure from the dying Peenemünde. Before von Braun left, he made it clear that I was to remain as long as I could be of service to the organization, then leave by the most expedient means available. But, as February ended and March began to drift by, the ways of getting to Bleicherode became fewer and fewer. As the relocation process approached completion, there were fewer groups or transports going south. Contact with *Mittelraum,* the new central location, was virtually nonexistent. Telephone communication was frequently disrupted, and there were few people traveling back in my direction who could carry any information.

Virtually everyone who was going had either left Peenemünde or was in the final throes of departure. There was nothing more for me to do. The Russians were at the gates of Swinemünde, less than fifty miles away, and the front lines weren't at all clear. It was time for me to leave.

First I had planned to join the Ordnance convoy unit which had been conducting the military launchings around Peenemünde. By going with them, I would rejoin the organization through Dornberger's staff, on the southern slopes of the Harz Mountains.

Then a more convenient opportunity presented itself and swung me into action. An Opel passenger car from the car pool was to be driven south on March 13. The night of the twelfth, I spent a pleasant evening with some friends from the plant. We had managed to acquire a bottle of reasonably good wine—in those

143

days that meant almost *any* wine—and we talked together for the last time. I strolled down the street leading from *Werk Süd* to *Werk Nord* after saying my final farewells to these people. The moon, just past full, shimmered down between the rows of quiet, deserted buildings. There were a few traces of light at the flak station and at the hospital, which I passed close by on the way to the gate, and *Haus 1*. I remember the pine trees, tall, silent, noble in the moonlight. How much longer, I wondered as I paused at the entrance to *Haus 1*. How much longer now? I thought how peaceful it was, and the vagrant wish passed through my mind that I could somehow make time stand still.

Next morning, after a restless night, I was up early. I wrote a hasty letter to Irmel to tell her I was finally leaving Peenemünde. There were all kinds of delays. I was ready, but the car was not: a mixup with the papers. Finally, about nine o'clock in the morning, the driver called and told me everything was straightened out; he had his gasoline ration cards, and was about to get the tank filled. Would I be ready?

I would be ready, I told him, and took my suitcase down to the street outside *Haus 1*. In a few moments, the Opel pulled up, and soon I was on my way. We did not talk much. I took one last, long, wistful look at Peenemünde as it receded behind us, and I knew, somehow, that I would never see that strange and wonderful place again. I turned quickly away and stared at the road ahead.

There were some spare parts waiting for us in Koserow, which we picked up. As soon as we had gotten the parts the driver took the car down a little side street to a shop that specialized in smoked herring. We got ourselves a bag full; they were fresh, still warm, a real delicacy.

Then, our stomachs comforted a little, we were on our way again: over the bridge at Wolgast, heading west first, and then gradually turning south through Jarmen, Demmin, Stavenhagen. It was an easy trip; the air was brisk, and the weather good.

But our progress was soon interrupted by more of those tragic bands of fugitives from the east, weary, homeless people crowding the highway with horses, carts, carriages, and wheelbarrows loaded with their few tattered worldly possessions. It was a painful experience, honking and jamming our way through these crowds of fleeing, frightened old men, women, and children.

Most of the trees along the highway had been cut down, and lay at the side of the road to be pulled across the highway when the invader came. At other spots, chains had been attached to the trees so that they could be pulled down at the right moment and the same thing accomplished.

By nightfall we were at Waren, on the Müritz Lake. The little town was completely blacked out, overcrowded, and the populace was absolutely terrified. We had a hard time finding any place to spend the night, but finally we located sleeping quarters in a private household.

We left Waren early the following morning, March 14, and now a sense of haste settled upon us. Our goal was Magdeburg, and we had lunch in the picturesque town of Burg. The restaurant was redolent with tradition, with its carved wooden furniture and leaded colored-glass windows. The food was good, and there was beer.

Magdeburg itself had been heavily bombed, and was to all intents and purposes completely destroyed. We made our way through the rubble to the local military car pool; my driver was still searching for some parts he had been instructed to get hold of somewhere, somehow. Suddenly, the air raid siren shrilled, abruptly terminating his efforts. We had no desire to be, caught in the middle of an air raid, and we hastened back to the Opel and raced out of Magdeburg. We arrived at Bleicherode rather late in the evening. My curiosity about what I would find at this new "test center" was at a peak. I was not really surprised at what I did find, though.

Extremely primitive headquarters had been set up in a former agricultural school. There was not much sense of order. We couldn't just bodily lift a whole engineering plant, drop it two hundred miles away, and expect it to continue functioning without interruption. I saw many familiar faces, and the general impression I got from conversations was that everybody felt about as I did.

I asked where von Braun was and learned, to my shock, that he was in the hospital. He had been in an automobile accident and had broken his right arm. There wasn't time to see him then.

I slept the night in a restaurant ballroom—an *Auffanglager,* "catcher camp," set up as a shelter for refugees. The floor had been covered with loose straw, not really very effective as a mattress; and the room was jammed with men, women, and crying children, and a fantastic assortment of battered and pathetic luggage.

What was happening to Germany? I knew the answer, but jammed in with that fragment of desperate humanity I couldn't erase the question from my mind. I fell into a deep exhausted sleep with the metronome beat of these words plaguing my soul for an answer.

The next morning was sunny, bright, almost cheerful. After great difficulty washing and shaving with the limited and primitive facilities, I wandered over to the school building again, and more and more familiar faces came into view. I found Fräulein Klinger, and talked with her for a few moments; she told me that I could have a "room" in the *Vergeltungs-Express*—the Vengeance Express as it was jokingly referred to. This was a train of ten or so sleeping cars that had been stationed at Heidelager, and later at Heidekraut, the Polish launching sites now in Russian hands. There the train had served as a sort of hotel on wheels for the launching crew officers. Now it was parked on a railroad siding at the potassium mine two miles outside of Bleicherode. Well, I thought, it's a pleasant day and the walk will do me good. To my surprise I had no difficulty in obtaining a compartment.

Having assured myself of decent sleeping facilities for the present, I walked back to town and searched out the housing office. I had another stroke of good luck: an engineer, living in a private room overlooking a shallow valley with the Harz Mountains in the distance, was being reassigned. His room would be available in a few days. I took it without hesitation.

I was now learning my way around the new "facility," and after a couple of hours of judicious and intensive questioning and searching, I even located the bicycle I had sent on ahead with one of the transports. This was most handy!

As yet, no offices had been set up. The closest thing was the converted school, which was the center of what activity existed and the source of whatever official or semi-official information there was to be had. A little inquiry revealed that some, but by no means all, of the technical groups were in Bleicherode proper. Many of them were scattered through nearby villages, an awkward arrangement, since transportation to and from these outlying areas was just about nonexistent.

I spent most of the day getting in touch with what groups I could locate. Generally, I found them in a state of semi-confusion, trying haphazardly, and really halfheartedly, to set themselves up in business. We all sensed the futility of it. I also managed to locate my own equipment and my packed correspondence, and got in touch with a number of prime personnel.

Later, I finally got over to the hospital and called on von Braun. He was in surprisingly good spirits, and talked eagerly about being up and out of the hospital in a matter of days. "The local authorities," he told me warmly, "have promised us the use of most of the administration building of the local power plant. This means we will have a modern building for ourselves, something better than I had hoped." His thoughts turned to the immediate problems. "But for now, let's do what we can to get our people settled and back into operation."

I left him with assurances that I would do what I could, and carried with me a few simple instructions. Even in the face of such hopelessness, I observed, von Braun's agile mind continued to function and to plan ahead.

But the state of confusion and uncertainty continued. Everything we did was little more than a gesture. Evenings I spent in the company of my friends and associates, in poorly lit restaurants, discussing the war and our chances of getting under way again. These were all rather discouraging conversations. Sometimes I spent an entire evening alone in my room, reading, or even catching up with some of the backlog of correspondence which my temporary separation from the main group had caused. But there was hardly any chance that the mail would ever be delivered. Fortunately for our peace of mind, there was a little movie theatre in Bleicherode; the films were old; most of them I had seen. But they provided some of the needed relaxation and escape from the grim reality that was closing in on us.

We had our share of air raid warnings, too. Many times we heard bombs falling and planes buzzing in the distance, accompanied by the rattle of machine-gun fire: *Jabos-Jagdbomber,* hedge-hopping fighter bombers, they called them. Yet through it all, the undaunted natives prepared for their annual Easter Festival, now fast approaching. This would be a lovely few hours "leave from war"—flowers, sunshine, balmy air.

Von Braun left the hospital on Wednesday, March 21, his arm still stiffly upright in a huge cast, and his temper by now on edge. He obviously felt he had been cooped up for too long, and wanted to get things moving. He occupied rooms in the home of one of the local cotton-mill owners, a beautiful, ultramodern house. Meantime, his headquarters in the powerplant building were set up, and he plunged us all into a series of meetings and discussions.

March 23 was his birthday, and there was a pleasant party at the house that evening; Dornberger and his wife, and other old friends and associates, were present. This was actually only one of many social evenings held there. We all seemed determined to maintain at least the façade of normal activity, social as well as business.

The following weekend, I bicycled to Bad Sachsa, ten miles distant, to visit Hartmut. He was stationed in the hotel where Dornberger had his headquarters.

"Let's go up to my place. My wife will make us some coffee!" he exclaimed, as I shook hands with him.

"Ersatz?" I grinned, and he shrugged, smiled, and nodded.

He had taken a few rooms in a house on a hilltop near the hotel. There we did have ersatz coffee and a bite to eat. We sprawled on the grass behind the house; the sun was warm and pleasant on us. But the news over the radio was cold and unpleasant. Hartmut switched it off. You couldn't turn off the fact of defeat, however. It was there, all around—obvious and inescapable.

"Listen," he said suddenly, and I sat up and cocked my ear. For a moment I thought he was referring to the ever-present rumble of cannon fire in the distance. But then I realized that there was something more, now—a buzzing, a distant growl, growing in loudness until it was a roar. I looked up, squinting against the dazzling blue, momentarily blinded by the sun.

I gasped. Up perhaps 20,000 feet was a flight of Allied bombers; hundreds upon hundreds of them, surrounded by the tiny points of their fighter escorts like dogs around a herd of sheep. I was aghast at the immensity of the formation, and I stared open-mouthed for a long while as they passed over.

"Berlin, I expect," Hartmut commented sadly.

Yes, Berlin, no doubt. I thought again of my many friends—and especially of my fiancée, Irmel. She was somewhere in the city that was slowly being turned to rubble. That evening, thoughtful and deeply worried, I bicycled home under brilliant moonlight.

The memory of those bombers stayed with me. I could not forget them, even while I worked, or put on the act of working, which was all it really was now. There was the constant reminder of the distant artillery which, faint and sporadic, daily grew louder. How much longer? I kept wondering. How much longer can it go on?

Defeat was inevitable. It was just as simple as that, and we all knew it whether we admitted it publicly or not. It was just a matter of time—and not much time at that. I wondered more and more why the German high command didn't capitulate. Surely they didn't believe their own propaganda about a "miracle weapon." The V-2 had been in operation over half a year by then. It hadn't silenced the artillery advancing across Germany. It hadn't grounded the fleets of bombers that daily pounded Germany's cities to dust and debris. What was to be gained by continuing to resist—other than more and more futile killing, more and more senseless destruction?

Then, on Easter Sunday afternoon, American tanks were sighted near Mühlhausen! That was scarcely twelve miles south of Bleicherode. I immediately went to von Braun's home. When I arrived, several other staff people were already there. The decision was quick, but this time, there was no deluding anybody. This was no longer relocation, this was flight.

"No equipment can be taken," said von Braun simply, and that was it, the end of our enterprise. "We will gather all our classified material and store it somewhere in an Alpine hideout," he added, "until it can be used again."

"By whom?" I wondered. It was not the first time the thought had come to us. To whom, the Russians or the Americans, would fall this treasure of engineering research and knowledge? It was more than just a question of who would catch us first, because we still had some element of choice.

We had, in point of fact, already exercised this choice by moving west, away from the Russians. Thus, the site of our new relocation was a logical continuation of our southern and westward movement—Oberammergau.

There was even a rumor that the Americans knew of our whereabouts, and were kept informed, not just by means of aerial reconnaissance but through channels. And it is a fact that, although Nordhausen, near the A-4 mass-production plant, was once attacked, no bomb ever fell on Bleicherode during the entire time of our residence there.

13

HIDE...

Thus, this period of troubled, futile waiting came to a precipitous halt, terminated by the need for sudden, intensive action. There was a scene of bustling activity: hasty preparations to depart, packing, discarding, storing (for what? we wondered), dispatching messages, arranging transport orders, authorizations, gasoline coupons, route planning, last minute instructions for disposal of the rocket development material that had to be left behind.

And most important to those of us at headquarters: what to do with the technical data we had brought with us from Peenemünde, a treasure trove of documents containing the sum and substance of the whole German rocket development effort. The quantity of material was too great to try and take with us. Even if this had not been so, there was now the real danger of destruction en route from air attack, capture by the enemy, or even having to abandon it along the way in case of transportation failure.

These documents were of inestimable value. Whoever inherited them would be able to start in rocketry at that point at which we had left off, with the benefit not only of our accomplishments, but of our mistakes as well—the real ingredient of experience. They represented years of intensive effort in a brand new technology, one which, all of us were still convinced, would play a profound role in the future course of human events.

The decision was quickly made. These documents—a cache of scientific information unlike any before in history—would be hidden somewhere in still-unoccupied Germany. How or where, no one knew. It just had to be done, and quickly. The job of executing this plan fell to me.

By the time this decision had been made it was late afternoon. I worked well into the night diagramming the locations of the various Peenemünde units now scattered around Bleicherode and neighboring villages, figuring the most expeditious pickup schedules, and poring over maps, evaluating the most likely areas in which I would find a suitable hiding place. Clear thought was plagued by the persistent realization that time was short. How short? How long before enemy tanks would rumble into Bleicherode? It could be just a matter of hours, a few days at the most. Already our escape routes were limited. And what about the front lines elsewhere in Germany? Which areas were still safe for a mission such as this? For months the shortage of material and human resources had slowly strangled Peenemünde. Now we suffered from a shortage of reliable information as well. There were no answers to these questions. We could only guess and hope. It was past midnight before I finally went to bed and fell into a troubled, restless slumber.

I rose early the following Monday morning, and found that I had little appetite. I immediately began the tedious task of alerting everybody to gather their material and ready it for pickup. Some I contacted by telephone; others required messengers. Because of the disorganized state of affairs, what should have been a simple matter became a monumental job.

I was still in the middle of this, operating out of von Braun's headquarters, when von Braun called me into his makeshift office. I sent a messenger off to the turbopump people and went on in to talk to him.

"How's it going?"

"As well as can be expected, I suppose." I shook my head. "Everything is just too scattered."

"Yes, it's pretty messed up." He nodded. "Another reason why we cannot be bothered with carrying anything with us. You stick to what you're doing, though. We can't afford to slip up on this." He handed me a sheet of paper. "Here is a letter of safe conduct. It will get you anywhere you want to go; but there is little I or anybody else can recommend to you in the way of where to hide the documents. You're on your own."

The letter stated simply that my mission was top secret; that it must be completed; and that I was to be accorded every assistance and not to be delayed along the way.

"Probably," von Braun continued, leaning forward, his elbows on the desk, "the best possibility is an old mine, or a cave—something of that sort. Perhaps the mining authorities at Clausthal can help. Other than that, as I say, I have no specific thoughts." He rose. "I've assigned Bernhard Tessmann to help you, and the car pool has been instructed to give you three 3-ton panel trucks. The VKN will provide you with a corporal and eight or ten men to handle the stuff." He was suddenly very serious. "There is just no time to lose."

I contacted Tessmann immediately, then finished alerting everybody, and gave instructions on the manner of packing: the pieces should not be too large, since handling was a major consideration, and the only material to be saved was that which would be essential should we resume our work. "Burn everything else, and above all, hurry!"

Next I set up a pickup schedule; after the manner of a railroad dispatcher, striving to make things happen in the most efficient possible sequence.

Our trucks arrived on schedule, and soon these three vehicles were moving steadily between headquarters and the various pickup points. Some of the trips were quick; some of them, to units located some miles outside of town, took exasperatingly long. By noon, however, I felt encouraged; things were in full swing. We worked steadily all day and late into the evening. About midnight, Tessmann and I called it a day and turned in. At seven the following morning, we were at it again.

The central gathering place was a room in the potassium mine administration building, and by midmorning Tuesday it was nearly full. It was obvious that three trucks were not going to be enough. Together Tessmann and I went down to the car pool and managed to shake loose two two-and-a-half-ton trailers, but not without considerable haranguing. Rain added to our troubles. By noon, it was pouring steadily.

"Well," I remarked, "at least this will slow down the Americans too."

We continued collecting material throughout the day. By late Tuesday night the job was done. We took only a moment to gaze in wonderment upon the astounding stack of paper before us, and then set about reloading the material onto the trucks and trailers in preparation for the journey. We continued working on into the night; I caught a couple of hours' sleep on a bench at the mine, and awoke still tired.

We had received good cooperation; most of the boxes were manageable, and everything went pretty smoothly. By eight o'clock Wednesday morning the trucks and the two trailers were loaded, and we were ready to go. I made a final tally of the checklist, and my heart fell: Aft End and Rudder Design had not come through. I groaned.

Fortunately, this unit had been set up in Bleicherode. We took a truck and trailer back to town. The rudder people themselves had long since departed, but had bequeathed us a huge blueprint storage file, locked, loaded, and weighing almost a ton. It took ten men to maneuver it out of the building and onto the trailer. We cursed those who had so cavalierly ignored our instructions.

But finally it was done, and we were on our way, by convoy, led by a passenger car with the driver and myself riding, followed by the three trucks, two of them with the trailers attached. In the truck cabs rode the eight others, including Tessmann and the drivers.

We followed secondary roads as much as we could in order to avoid as much traffic congestion and interference from the authorities as possible. We headed toward the Harz Mountains.

The rain, which had continued to hamper our loading operations, stopped at last. We moved steadily, but slowly, since the trucks were heavily loaded. Bad Sachsa was empty and quiet as we passed by; Dornberger's group was gone. There was little conversation and virtually no stops as we moved northward toward Herzberg and Osterode.

We had been on the road a couple of hours without any incident when suddenly the roar of planes burst upon us. "Jabos!" the driver shouted and swung the car into the ditch under some trees, just a moment before the planes flashed overhead.

They didn't see us and were quickly out of sight. The pattern was repeated again and again. One of these times we would not be so lucky. After half a dozen such close shaves, we decided to carry a lookout to watch our rear. Fortunately, the front fender design of the Opel truck was such that a man could ride there in reasonable comfort. The position provided a clear view of the sky behind us. When we started rolling again it was with a man riding in this lookout position. The observer task was rotated.

This worked out pretty well, and we were able to drive off the highway in time to avoid being spotted. Once, as we were passing through a small village, the observer shouted a warning, and we swung under the leafy protection of a grove of trees. But we had hardly stopped when a horde of angry villagers descended upon us, shouting, waving their fists.

"Get your trucks out of here! Get out! You'll make them shoot up the village!"

They had a point and I sympathized with them. But we stayed where we were until the planes had passed on. When we moved out of the village, the imprecations of the villagers followed after us.

About noon, we came to the little town of Lerbach, a small community nestled in a narrow, gulchlike valley—a locale, we decided, which would be particularly inaccessible to the bullets of strafing planes. We found a clear area and parked the trucks.

Clausthal was only five miles further ahead. I left Tessmann to arrange quarters for the men in Lerbach, and I took the car up to Clausthal. This town was the heart of German mining engineering. My destination was the headquarters of the Supreme Federal Mining Authority. Inside the old building, I found myself in a dignified hall that radiated venerable age. It reminded me a bit of a little palace, and the reserved, aloof old man whom I met when I asked to see the *Oberbergrat,* the chief of the mining authority, completed the picture. I was direct and to the point.

"Herr *Bergrat,* I have in my possession several truckloads of the very highest classified military documents in Germany." I presented my letter to him. "As you can see from this, our task is to find a place in which these can be safely hidden. This instruction comes from the High Command."

The *Bergrat* was the epitome of politeness, distant but not unfriendly, a pillar of dignity in a situation where dignity had all but ceased to exist, a gray-haired, black-suited old man with a metal-capped cane. He held the paper in one hand and leaned on his cane with the other while he read.

"What we need," I continued, "is a place off the main highway, on a side road, perhaps, a hole in a mountain, an abandoned mine. Something with rail tracks leading into it."

He looked up from the paper and shook his head. "There is nothing here that meets those requirements. These mines are all vertical, equipped with elevators. And all, I assure you, are well known." Again he shook his head, and handed the paper back to me. "I'm very sorry. May I suggest you try our suboffice in Goslar? Mr. Cornelius may be able to help you."

I was sorely disappointed, and not a little desperate. I had really pinned my hopes on this man. I took time out only to eat and then raced the small passenger car along the twisting mountain road to Goslar. Once I thought I heard the distant echo of machine guns, though I couldn't be sure. I worried about the trucks, and hurried on. I had no trouble locating Mr. Cornelius.

He listened thoughtfully while I stated our need again. He was friendly, and he wanted to help, but he, too, was very sorry.

"You see, the mines here are already full of government stuff from Berlin. There'd be no way, either, of keeping it apart from your material. I have a suggestion, though—why don't you try the people up at Wernigerode?"

Suddenly I was angry, utterly furious with the frustration of the situation.

"Here I stand, with the most important documents in Germany!" I exploded. "And I can't even find a place to put them. Nothing in those mines approaches what we've got in significance—."

I wheeled and stamped toward the exit. Cornelius called after me.

"Wait a minute . . . maybe there is something. I had forgotten . . ."

I whirled and faced him, angered and impatient.

Where were the tanks now, I wondered, that had been reported near Mühlhausen just three days earlier? Where was the rest of the front? Suppose our trucks at Lerbach were captured while I was being shuffled from one mining official to the next! Cornelius appeared truly apologetic.

"There's an abandoned mine in Dörnten. There have been so many like you lately, I just didn't think about it. It's not in the mountains . . . but I think it might be suitable."

"Can I see it?"

"Of course." He reached for a piece of paper and began to sketch on it. "I'll give you directions——."

"I'd like you to come along and introduce me."

"Well. . . ." He smiled. "Why not? There isn't much I can do here these days, anyway."

I hurried him out to the car. We drove by his house, so that he could tell his wife he had left and would be back in a few hours. Then we were on our way, driving west along the highway to Hildesheim. About three miles away from the Harz Mountains, we turned off to the right on a bumpy dirt road; through the small village of Dörnten; then onto another road through open fields and gently rolling countryside. Suddenly, the elevator tower of a mine rose into view. It had been a good-sized operation. A number of buildings were clustered around the tower. I stopped the car.

"This is it," Cornelius said. "Shaft *Georg Friedrich*. That vertical shaft," he pointed, "hasn't been used for several years. The ore here is of low quality and isn't economical with the current shortage of men and energy. We just keep a few maintenance people here. There is another mine in that shallow hill behind the tower, discontinued some years ago."

"Who's in charge here?"

"A man named Nebelung."

"Do you know where he lives?"

"Yes."

I started the car and shifted gears. As I did I heard the drone of bombers in the distance. "Let's go see him."

Cornelius directed me.

"Nebelung has been here for a long time," he added. "He's too old to be drafted, and has tried to keep things in good shape until the equipment can be used again." He shrugged. "Who knows when?" Then he gestured. "Here we are—third house."

We had come up to a row of about a dozen "company" houses, minimal, all-the-same structures provided by the company. They were not too bad looking, but certainly lacked the colorful appeal that characterized the rural buildings in the area, with their happy jumble of styles. The whole housing area was landscaped and sprinkled with trees bursting with fresh green color and showering flowers.

Nebelung and his wife were an elderly and very friendly couple. It was apparent from the outset that Nebelung was eager to help us. The moment Cornelius had finished describing the reason for our visit, he was immediately ready to show us the mine. We waited for a moment while he changed into work clothes, and then followed him over the fields to the mine, through the service buildings, and finally to the entrance to the tunnel itself, nestled at the end of a little gulch butting against the foot of a low, gently sloping hill. Rails led into the darkness. There were a couple of switches and a loading ramp. It was too good to believe, but this was it! For the first time in several days I smiled. Now, if only the trucks and their precious cargo were still safe.

Nebelung then took us over to the supply building. There we got some battery lamps and miners' hats, and thus armed, we followed the rails into the mountain.

Galleries branched off every now and again, on either side. About a thousand feet into the mountain, Nebelung stopped and flashed his torch to the left, revealing another of these small galleries, this one with a floor that sloped slightly uphill.

"Up there used to be our powder magazine," he explained. "Where we stored our explosives—and these had to be kept absolutely dry, you know."

We went perhaps a hundred yards into this gallery, when suddenly it came to an end, blocked by a heavy, ironclad door.

"Here it is," said Nebelung, obviously pleased. "It's elevated, and this part of the mountain is particularly dry."

There was a room about twenty-five feet square, and some twelve feet high. It was perfect.

"There isn't much I can say," I remarked finally, turning to my companions. "It's ideal—it couldn't be better. All that remains is to get the material in."

"I think I can help you there, also." Nebelung smiled as he led us back toward the exit. "We've got a small electric-battery locomotive. It probably needs recharging, but I'll have it ready for you tomorrow. It should do for carting the material into the mine."

It was dark when I arrived in Lerbach. The trucks were intact, and the soldiers were having a good time at the village inn, something for which I really couldn't blame them. I scouted around until I found Tessmann, and then over dinner and ersatz coffee we laid out a plan of action.

"Tonight," I said as we rose, "a good long rest. It may be our last for a while." He nodded in agreement, and we went our ways.

I did indeed sleep long and well. Next morning, after an early breakfast, Tessmann and I gathered the men together. We all sprawled on the grass by the parked trucks, while I explained our plan.

"We will drive the trucks to an old quarry close to Goslar. It will make an excellent center of operations. It's located in a narrow part of the valley and should be safe from Jabos. When nightfall comes, I'll drive the first truck and trailer myself to the hiding place. With the exception of Tessmann, all of the rest of you will be locked inside the truck. That way, you will be able to say with complete honesty that you have no idea where we have hidden these documents. Two of you will remain behind, one for each of the remaining trucks, just in case. . . . When we've unloaded the first truck, I'll come back and pick up the next, and then the third."

I thought wryly: This is how I started the war, driving trucks!

Once all the questions had been answered, we boarded the trucks and were on our way. By noon we were at the quarry and parked. The next few hours were really maddening. Waiting, I suppose, is always that way; but now I could not shake from my mind the picture of the steadily advancing enemy, engulfing Germany.

I shifted nervously from lounging in the cab to brief exploratory strolls around the quarry, and I read a little. I had some letters from Irmel, too, which I kept in my pocket. Irmel in bomb-shattered Berlin! The dull, earth-shaking thuds of the rolling bomb carpets at Peenemünde flashed back to mind with a surge of fear. So many of these had fallen, continued to fall, on Berlin. Was she alive? How would we ever get together again?

Late in the afternoon, I made an advance trip to an SS post that stood between us and our goal, showed the officer in charge our credentials, and explained that the three trucks would be passing back and forth, individually, during the night. This saved a lot of trouble.

Finally, it was night. We checked out the first truck, loaded the men into the back, and without lights began our trip. We drove slowly through Goslar and past the SS station, then on to Dörnten.

I pulled the truck up at the siding, and the men piled out. Immediately we began unloading the boxes. Nebelung had placed flatcars there for us, with the promised engine. As soon as we had emptied the truck, I left Tessmann in charge and made the trip back alone. It was a lonely journey indeed, with only the jumble of thoughts, fear, and questions that now constantly tumbled through my mind as companions.

Three hours later I was back at the mine with the second truck; there was no one outside. It was almost two hours before the sweating, tired crew emerged from the mine. They rested for a while, without much conversation. Then we unloaded, and I was off for the third truckload.

It was nearly dawn when I arrived with the third truck, the one without a trailer, carrying, in addition to the load of papers, the two men I had left with the trucks at the quarry. The sun was tinting the sky by the time this was unloaded.

Until almost eleven in the morning, we worked at hard physical labor. The boxes were heavy. The gallery leading to the storage room was narrow, and uphill. The real monster, of course, was the one-ton filing cabinet which the rudder people had bequeathed us. For the second time, they were the recipients of many bitter recriminations.

The room was just about full when the last box was in place. I stood back and surveyed the results through bleary eyes. Mission accomplished, I thought, and all of a sudden I was dead tired. I looked around, and I saw my weariness reflected in the faces of the others, leaning against the wall, squatting on the floor, or standing with hands on hips, covered with sweat and utterly disarrayed.

"Come along," said Nebelung, "to the shower rooms."

This was the first good news in a long time.

After that most welcome shower, which washed away at least some of the exhaustion along with the dirt, we were treated to a meal which Nebelung had arranged for us in the now-deserted mine lunchroom. Never had simple bean soup tasted so good.

While we ate, Nebelung discussed the problem of further concealing our hideaway. He agreed to dynamite the gallery leading to the storeroom, promising to begin the operation that very night.

"Fine," I nodded. "I will come back tomorrow to see if everything worked out."

I felt great confidence in Nebelung; he had come through on every count so far, and seemed completely trustworthy.

Our next problem was to find a place to sleep. A decent bed was now our greatest need. But this was something difficult to come by. There was absolutely nothing in Goslar, so we had to go elsewhere. Not west—toward the battlefront and in a direction where there were few villages. Instead, we began a weary journey east, all of us on the edge of sleep, along the northern rim of the Harz Mountains, an area studded with resorts and vacation spots.

We moved slowly along a relatively good highway, encountering surprisingly little traffic and no military activity whatsoever. We were approaching Bad Harzburg when we spotted a policeman at an intersection.

I pulled over, showed him our pass, and explained our need, which I'm sure he could read on our faces. We were in luck; he assured us that in his village, a couple of miles off the main highway, we would be taken care of. He directed us.

Within an hour, we all had places to stay. Everybody was very pleasant. The people seemed to want to be as pleasant as possible as long as they could. We were all provided with meals and beds. I slept deeply.

The following day was Saturday. About noon, Tessmann and I drove back to the mine to inspect the results of the dynamiting. It was not really satisfactory; rocks blasted from the roof had formed a heap below, but it was still an easy matter to clamber over this into the storage room. I urged Nebelung to finish the job, and he promised that they would blast again that night. We took him at his word, and after a meal at the village inn, we started back toward Goslar. Just as we were entering the town, we heard airplane engines and machine-gun fire. I careened the car to a stop, and we dove for the ditch beside the highway.

The firing continued almost uninterruptedly for about five minutes; but fortunately the target seemed to be elsewhere. Soon the planes were gone, and we continued on our way.

That night I instructed Tessmann to take the trucks and the men back to Bleicherode.

"Be sure and hang on to one truck, though," I told him. "Remember we've got to pick up some of the professor's stuff. I'll stay here with the car, and Monday I'll check on the mine again."

The following morning my driver and I bade Tessmann and the others goodbye. It was a quiet Sunday and, after the trucks had passed from sight, I took a stroll around the village. Idling, I studied some maps, and discovered that nearby was Eckertal where my old friend Sergeant Kessler now lived.

He was assigned to a government bureau there. It had all happened at Peenemünde only a short while after my arrival, when a representative of another agency had asked if I knew of an experienced metal craftsman in the service. I figured I owed Kessler a favor considering that his cleverness had helped me make the contact which led to my Peenemünde reassignment. I gave Kessler's name, and to my surprise, he had gotten the job. I rifled through my notebook, and sure enough, there was his address!

That Sunday afternoon was a great reunion for both of us, and the tales that were told ceased only when our thoughts turned to our concern for what the next few days would bring. I was most reluctant to say goodbye to Kessler and his wife that afternoon, but of course it had to be.

I had hardly arrived at my quarters when the policeman who had earlier been so helpful to us appeared, dressed in civilian clothes, obviously agitated.

"American troops are entering Goslar." He gripped my arm. "That means they'll be here . . . when? Maybe tonight! What can I do?"

We discussed it for a while; he obviously needed to talk it out.

"I don't think I should run. What good would it do? And I don't think I've done anything to feel wrong about—my family is here, I own this house. . . ."

"Running would just mean a delay, don't you think?" I ventured.

This was what he wanted to hear, naturally.

"Yes, you're right. I'll stay—I'll wear civilian clothes and wait for them."

However, there was no reason for me to remain. I had to get back to Bleicherode. I would have to trust Nebelung to get the blasting job done properly. I rounded up my driver. We gathered our few things and left.

The bad news had obviously preceded us. In the windows of every house along the way, and on through Bad Harzburg, hung white flags and occasionally red crosses. How different from the many National Holidays of just a few years back when, instead of red crosses, brightly colored swastikas swayed in the breeze!

We turned south from Harzburg, crossing the Harz Mountains toward Braunlage. Night fell. The winding mountain roads, driving without lights, and the overpowering presence of the dense, dark forests were a grinding strain on my already edgy nerves. Suddenly, as we approached Nordhausen, the sound of heavy anti-aircraft fire cut through the air, followed by bomb concussions, the flash of explosions and the dazzling glare of flares shimmering above the treetops.

We pulled over to the side of the road, and stopped among ghostly burned-out cars and trucks that lined the way in chaotic disarray. *Jabos* had found a military convoy and ripped it to shreds. Now, the twisted metal flickered grotesquely in the light of distant fires. My thoughts kept going back to Berlin. Soon we were on our way again, spelling each other at the wheel and grabbing what sleep we could.

The next town was Braunlage, blacked out, silent, and asleep. There was no sign of life as we felt our way without lights through its narrow ancient streets. Suddenly, above the purr of the car's engine I heard a raucous growling clatter. Immediately ahead, a monstrous shadow loomed up. It was a great tracked self-propelled gun. My heart skipped a beat. Then I realized it was one of ours, German. But it was coming right at us! On that narrow street I could not see how we could possibly pass. I swerved the car up against the wall of the house next to the street. I didn't even have time to back up when the monster was upon us. The barrel of its great gun swung over us, and its track clawed by with but a fraction of an inch to spare. I am not even sure the driver had seen us.

In the early morning hours, we came upon the smoldering wreckage of Nordhausen, whose destruction we had viewed from a distance. It was frightening.

An old man at a service station told us Bleicherode had already been captured. There was a new sense of urgency as we headed for Sangerhausen instead, in hopes of encountering some member of the Manufacturing Department. Werner Kuers, my old friend from test planning days, was there, and he told us the Bleicherode report was false; the town had not yet fallen. He had in fact just talked on the telephone to one of our people there.

"I judge," he remarked, "that the fronts are moving very slowly right now. I don't think the Americans have advanced much since the Mühlhausen rumor circulated and you left with our papers."

Back at Bleicherode, we found everything quiet. Most of our people had been gone for several days. And now was no time for me to tarry. My main assignment ended with the return of the trucks and trailers. My orders now were to load the third truck with von Braun's things, and some supplies which had been left behind, plus anything of my own that I felt merited transportation, and to move on to Oberammergau.

I had a bit of difficulty getting back the truck Tessmann had reserved, but I finally managed, plus one of our truck drivers, a fellow named Hans.

Shortly after this, Paul, one of our lookout crew on the classified documents mission, arrived.

"Can I join you?" he asked simply.

I shrugged.

"As far as I'm concerned, it's all right. What about your unit, the VKN?"

It was his turn to heave his shoulders.

"To hell with it. I don't care."

"Then you're welcome—on condition you continue as our lookout man."

He laughed. "It's a deal."

That night was my last in Bleicherode. Hans and Paul were to pick me up at seven in the morning, and we would wind our way down the narrowing corridor of crumbling Germany to our uncertain rendezvous with destiny.

14

...AND SEEK

Events from this point forward assume an almost dreamlike, even nightmare quality in my memory. It seemed I was running, running . . . as though in some futile attempt to escape the inevitable. Nobody could say what was going to happen tomorrow or the next week. It just seemed necessary to keep going.

On that April 10, 1945, I was awake before seven. I felt quite rested, all things considered. I shaved and enjoyed a good breakfast. Outside, the sun peered feebly through clinging mists. A half dozen wooden boxes, some suitcases, and a few scattered items were all that was left to me in the way of personal possessions.

It was now seven-thirty. I paced nervously between my upstairs room and the front door. Each time it was just the same: the hilly street was quiet. Where was the truck? Suddenly the door burst open, and the landlady's aunt, who lived down the street, came rushing into the house.

"Last night one of my friends came back from Haynrode." Haynrode was only a few miles east. She talked excitedly. "They've got their white flags out, and he heard machine-gun fire nearby before he left. They'll be here today, won't they?"

Now I was really uneasy. It was nearly eight o'clock. Could Paul and Hans have left without me? I immediately rejected the thought. But what had happened? A jolt of fear shot through me. Maybe the car-pool sergeant had backed down! That decided me. I went out, climbed on my bicycle, and rode down to the car pool. Nobody there . . . maybe the mine. I pedaled rapidly in that

direction, and then, around a turn in the road, I saw them: they
were eating breakfast in the shade of the truck. I halted the bicycle,
and stared. This was probably the only time in all those agonizing
days that I really lost my temper at anybody—something about
their casualness contrasted with my increasing concern. Nor did
I attempt to hide my opinion, for which I felt a little sorry afterward.

"We got a little drunk last night, Herr Huzel," said Paul,
obviously very embarrassed. "We didn't turn in until late, and
we overslept—." He and Hans were very sheepish, and my anger
began to evaporate.

"Okay, okay," I snapped, waving my hand impatiently. "Now,
let's get moving. Hurry up, get your things."

It actually took only a few seconds for them to gather their
belongings, while I got the truck started. We slid the bicycle in
the back and piled into the cab. I slammed the truck in gear,
gunned the motor, and we were off. At von Braun's, we picked
up some suitcases and a few suits and other gear. Paul kept
apologizing.

"Herr Huzel, I feel responsible as hell. Here it is nine o'clock,
and we're already two hours late—."

"Forget it, forget it." We climbed back into the truck and
swung toward my rooming house. "All that's important now is
that we keep moving."

On the way, we halted for a moment at the supply house and
picked up a 50-pound keg of butter and a large wooden box of
Italian sweet vermouth that had been kept in reserve for occasions when management had to entertain some officials.

As we were rounding the last corner toward my house, the
terrifying chatter of a machine-gun salvo burst upon our ears.

"My God!" exclaimed Hans. "They're here!"

I brought the truck to a squealing halt in front of my place,
and we clambered out.

"Step on it! *Avanti!*" I yelled.

The machine-gun fire came again, closer, only a few hundred
yards away. We rushed into the house, down to the basement, and
began bringing the boxes up. Once Hans stumbled and fell on
the steps, cursing loudly. I picked up the box he had dropped and

took it out to the car. Another machine-gun burst and rifle fire barked simultaneously as we threw the last suitcase in back and slammed the doors. Yelling goodbye to my landlady, we roared away.

"Which way?" shouted Paul.

"Head north," I replied. "We'll take a wide northeast arc around the Americans, and then swing south."

As we rushed into the dissipating mists, I thought of the electric hotplate I had forgotten, as well as the box with the newspaper clippings and a few books, things which had seemed so precious, but which were now suddenly trivial.

As we moved out of sound of the machine-gun fire, the sun burst out in full glory. We were heading north again through the beautiful Harz Mountains. We would swing over to Halle, then Leipzig, and south to Oberammergau—if we made it all the way before the end came. It was a magnificent day; and through it all I kept doubting reality—*fleeing through my own country?*

The machine-guns at Bleicherode were American. What about the Russians? The ring was closing about us. And what about Irmel, in Berlin? I writhed under the thought. So many things to worry about, too many things.

We avoided principal highways as much as possible. Even on the lesser roads, we encountered military activity. Everywhere little units were setting up road blocks, defense establishments, vain efforts to hold back the inevitable. Always our "Secret Material" pass got us through. *Destination: Classified,* it proclaimed. We gave rides to many hitchhikers—soldiers occasionally, who were always picked up at the next road block—or just wandering souls with some uncertain destination in mind, fleeing like we were but with tragically less purpose.

Soon we approached Blankenburg, the little town at the "Devil's Wall" where I had gone to high school for half a year, during the French occupation of the Ruhr so many years before. The wonderful people with whom I had boarded during those days still lived here, and I could not deny myself the pleasure of stopping, to say hello and shake the old man's hand. I suppose my feelings were somewhat akin to that universal expression of *Kameraderie* which these declining days had so brought out.

Quedlinburg was next, ten miles farther east. This too held memories for me . . . and hope. Irmel had family friends in Quedlinburg, and in the old days she had spent many summers with them. Perhaps she would be there now, out of the holocaust of Berlin. There was a strong road block at the town's edge.

"We've just received an air raid warning," said the sergeant in charge. "You'll have to wait."

I pulled the truck over to the side of the road. "You fellows stay here. I'm going to walk ahead and see if I can find Irmel."

I walked on into Quedlinburg. While I was still walking, the all clear sounded and people began to emerge from shelters and cellars. At the city hall I got the address of Irmel's friends and finally found the right house. Irmel was not there.

"But we got a letter from her only a few days ago. From Berlin. She said everybody was all right."

That was something, but hardly satisfying. Who could tell how long it might be or what might intervene before I would see her again? I thanked them and began the weary trek back to the truck. My friends were naturally impatient.

"Sorry. I didn't realize it would take so long." I was a little gruff. "Let's get going."

There was some hesitation.

"We've been talking something over—" began Paul.

I was already entering the cab. I turned. "Well?"

"Herr Huzel," said Hans, "my parents live in Bergwitz. That's near Wittenberg, you know." He hesitated. "I know it's not exactly according to plan, but why don't we go there for the night? It would mean at least one comfortable night's sleep, and probably something good to eat."

"That's a lot farther east than we want to go, though," I demurred. I scratched my chin. "But what can we lose?"

"Herr Huzel," interjected Paul, "who knows what will happen next? Hans may never get another chance to see his parents!"

"Of course." I smiled and got into the cab. "Let's go!"

As the truck roared into life and the others clambered in beside me, I added:

"It will be late, though. And we've got a gasoline supply problem."

Hans grinned.

"My father owns an automobile repair business. He can get us some. Our reserve cans will carry us to Bergwitz."

"Well, let's not lose any time!" We were rolling again.

Just as we were leaving, an immense formation of bombers passed high above headed in the direction of Berlin. Another rolling carpet for the beleaguered city! Why hadn't Irmel left Berlin? There was the family, of course, and their business, which even in times like these had to be kept going. But still . . .

I was hardly aware of the passing of the miles or of time. We were approaching Aschersleben when the rattle of machine-gun fire jerked me out of my reverie. *Jabos!* Quickly I swung the truck off the highway, and we piled out and scrambled into the ditch. By now, this procedure was an almost automatic reflex action.

We hunched down as far as we could into the ditch. The roar and buzz of the planes became louder and more ominous, and the gunfire almost unbroken. I peeked out. All along the road, cars had stopped. Doors hung open, left ajar in the haste of evacuation. No one stirred.

Now came the sound of small bombs farther away. There was a railroad switchyard nearby. Suddenly, the concussion of bombs was joined by a chatter and a bang, most irregular, of what seemed to be small arms, fired from the ground. Then there were heavier reports; this continued uninterruptedly.

"They've hit an ammunition train!" exclaimed Hans, in a hoarse whisper.

The planes pulled away, the machine-gun fire ceased, the drone of the engines faded. Soon we were on our way again. I mused as to the possible destination of the others on the road.

Late that evening, it was a hearty welcome, and a touching one too, that we received from Hans' parents in Bergwitz. They did everything in their power to make us comfortable. In short order we found ourselves sitting down to a fine big meal, and the then almost-unheard-of treat of good wine afterward.

Finished, we relaxed with more of the wine and talked. For Hans it was an exhilarating, albeit nostalgic evening. For Paul, it was a last chance to relax. But I could not keep my mind off Berlin, and Irmel. And an idea began to take form.

I visualized the map of Germany. Berlin was just 65 miles from where we sat, and we were on a main highway. I sipped some more wine. We could make it in a few hours.

Suddenly, a shattering explosion shook the house. Bombs close by. Everybody was abruptly quiet. We looked up at the ceiling and waited. Gradually, the sound of the lone airplane faded.

"Maybe someone left their shades up with the light on," Hans' mother suggested.

"Just a random throw, probably left over from Berlin," added his father.

Now was as good a time as any.

"My fiancée is in Berlin . . ." I started, clearing my throat.

They all listened attentively. To my surprise, nobody demurred. "I know it's dangerous," I concluded, "but any move we make is dangerous and I would like to get her out of there while I can. The Russians . . ." I said grimly. Even here reports of their extreme brutality, particularly to women, had filtered through. "Whatever happens, I'd like to be sure she falls into the same hands as I do."

Hans shrugged.

"You're the boss, Herr Huzel. You give us the word, and we'll come along."

I shook my head.

"That isn't enough. Soon nobody will be the boss. And it's certainly not strictly legal."

Hans laughed.

"Is our presence *here* legal?"

"That's true." I became silent.

Paul got up and put his hand on my shoulder. "I'm for it. Everything's worked out all right so far, hasn't it?"

"How about gasoline?" I asked. "We're out of ration cards."

"True," agreed Hans. "But my father can help us with a few liters"—the old man nodded—"and later on, well, we'll just find other ways of getting what we need. Let's not worry about that."

That settled it. The three of us would go to Berlin together.

The next day we would arise late, relax for the day at Hans' home, and then leave about six in the evening.

Shortly after nine in the evening of the eleventh of April we were sitting in the truck, parked in the Potsdam woods just on the edge of Berlin, making a last-minute check of our plans. My scheme was to ride the bicycle, still stowed in the back of the truck, on into Berlin.

"Relax," I said as I swung aboard the bicycle. "This may take all night."

Soon I was pedaling down familiar streets, through the center of Potsdam and on toward Berlin. My route took me along the famous straight AVUS racetrack which leads into the center of Charlottenburg—a sort of freeway which under ordinary circumstances was forbidden to bicycles. I was nearing its end when the shriek of an air raid siren shattered the still night air. At that moment, I was right at the exposition and stadium area, the site of the Olympic games almost ten years earlier.

The air raid siren continued its frightful wail. A policeman directed me to the nearest public shelter. I took the bike in with me. The few people in the shelter were very quiet and, it seemed to me, thoroughly dispirited. It was past midnight before the raid ended and I could venture out again.

Once in Berlin, I was able to make use of the cycle strips, which are provided along all the major streets in the city. This simplified travel in the pitch dark of the night. Irmel and her family lived in an apartment in northern Berlin, and it was well after one o'clock in the morning—April 12, 1945—when I rattled on the door and was greeted by startled and sleepy faces. It was the first time I had seen Irmel in many months. Though surprised and still sleepy I could see she was well and unharmed. When she realized it was really I, tears welled up in her eyes. I took her in my arms, and it was minutes before either of us could speak a coherent sentence.

But everything was all right. As soon as the household was awake and the immediate surprise of my visit had passed, I told them why I had come.

"I want to take Irmel out of Berlin with me. Our staff has relocated to the south."

Even as I spoke, I thought of her parents. What of them? Yet I could not hope to take them also; one must be logical even in matters of duty and responsibility. They knew exactly what I was thinking, and they were as happy as I to see her out of the number one bombing target in Germany.

"But we must leave without delay," I warned them.

"Of course," agreed her father, and packing began immediately.

As they prepared her bags, I told Irmel that we had best go back to Potsdam by the *S-Bahn*.

"That's not as easy as you might think, Dieter," she cautioned me. "You need a special pass."

"For the *S-Bahn?*"

She nodded.

"For the *S-Bahn*, for the streetcars, for everything."

I smiled.

"Well, maybe it's not so big an obstacle as you think. I'll be back directly."

While they finished the packing, I went to the nearest police station, a couple of blocks away, and with my "Classified Material" pass, obtained the necessary *S-Bahn* Special Pass for Irmel, myself, and the bicycle.

It was four-thirty, and daylight was beginning to bleach the sky, when Irmel and I finally left the apartment. Her mother went as far as the Potsdam terminal with us. The trip took two hours, an inordinately long time. We had to switch trains twice. How the once-fine Berlin transportation system had deteriorated under the effects of the raids!

After a final goodbye, we started walking the mile-and-a-half to the truck, using the bicycle as a sort of cart for the suitcases. When we arrived, Hans and Paul were asleep. They were not even aware of how long I had been gone.

After the introductions all around, Hans and Paul freshened up a bit, and we all had something to eat. Meanwhile, I arranged the interior of the truck into as comfortable a sleeping compartment as possible.

Then we were on our way back to Wittenberg the same way we had come: the three of us, Hans, Irmel and myself in the cab, with Paul occupying his usual fender post. Hardly twelve hours had passed, but changes were already noticeable. There was now considerable activity around the bridges by military demolition teams, and twice we observed similar preparations along the road. The number of roadblocks and checking stations had increased sharply. Without special passes, we would never have made it.

Through Wittenberg to Bergwitz we drove, where our welcome from Hans' parents was warm, but fraught with concern. The radio had reported only a short while before that American forces were advancing on Leipzig. We must flee Bergwitz immediately.

Hans' father gave us the last of his gas, and his mother gave us a large bag of sandwiches. It was a sad parting for Hans, who could not know whether he would ever see his family again. Initially we followed the main highway toward Leipzig, but at Düben we swung off in a southeasterly direction, thus skirting Leipzig to the east. We passed on through Wurzen, Lausick, and Altenburg. I had never before seen this country, and I regretted the circumstances of the trip.

We were forced to dodge *Jabos* incessantly. Paul standing *Jabo* watch really earned his keep. During those frightened moments, hiding in the ditch, wondering if this time would be the last time, I thought bitterly that this beautiful country was no place to be dodging bullets. The calmness with which the people on foot, usually women, would casually step under trees, or behind houses, when these strafing attacks came along, bespoke the hardships they had endured and the adaptability of the human spirit.

At Altenburg we managed to locate a *Kaserne*—headquarters of a motorized unit—where we sought out the cognizant officer to arrange for some gas. But he was blind to the words of our all-purpose pass and deaf to our arguments. After wrangling for half an hour, we gave up.

Typical April weather now descended on us, sunshine alternating with showers. Just as we climbed the heights south of Altenburg, the sun broke through and shimmered dazzlingly on the wet highway. Before us stretched the smashed remains of a military convoy: at least a hundred cars and trucks, wrecked and scattered on either side of the highway. Irmel caught her breath at the sight of it.

Some of the vehicles still smoldered. Others on the road ignored the wreckage. As long as the air was clear of planes, everyone kept hurrying toward his own particular destination. We pulled over near some trucks that looked as though they had merely been abandoned, hoping to find some gasoline. But these, too, had been burnt out. There was no gasoline to be had.

Nowhere did we see any bodies. Apparently the remainder of the convoy had departed, taking the survivors and dead with them. There was the smell of burnt rubber in the air.

As we drove along, our spirits lifted, however. After all, we were still alive, and our truck was still operating. We had long, pleasant sunlit stretches uninterrupted by any bitter reminders of war. We talked about many things that had nothing to do with the war. For Irmel and me the prospect of a future together brightened with every mile that passed.

But the fuel gauge kept creeping lower. Normally, we would not have been concerned, for there was plenty for the journey. But under the circumstances, we had to have a reserve, for there was no guarantee our route would be as direct as we planned. Even the twenty-liter "last resort" reserve tank in the back was not sufficiently reassuring.

We stopped at every gas station we came to, always without success. No coupons, no gas. Finally, on a side street in the approach to Plauen, a woman operating a station was impressed with our "Classified Material" pass, and she gave us twenty liters. We signed a slip of paper promising to send ration cards as soon as possible. "We promise!" We both knew this was a ritual, a formality, and that unless there were a miracle we would not be able to keep our promise.

We avoided Plauen itself and stopped at Auerbach, farther on. One of the stations that had refused us gasoline had given us the name of a ration card official in Auerbach, and we intended to look him up. It was past five in the afternoon when we arrived, so his office was closed. Undaunted, I telephoned him. I explained the situation, and he agreed to come back to the office "after I've finished supper."

It was a good-sized supper, apparently, for it was nearly two hours before he arrived. His offer was for twenty liters.

"That's not enough," I said firmly. "We need more." I flashed our multiple-purpose pass. "We're on strict orders. We've got to get to Oberammergau, and must not be interfered with."

"All right, all right," he said, waving his hands helplessly. "Thirty liters, then, but that's all I can do."

I accepted this offer grumpily. Actually, I was delighted; this would probably get us over the hump. We redeemed these cards at the next filling station, and drove through the night, Hans and I alternating at the wheel. We had to get out of this area as quickly as possible, because it seemed clear that the Allied intention was to cut Germany in half across the corridor down which we were driving. We all took turns resting in back, which proved fairly comfortable under the circumstances.

The driving was becoming a grind, however. The sky was cloudy, our lights were dimmed almost to the point of uselessness, and we had to be extremely alert to avoid an accident. There was, fortunately, little traffic.

We went through Brambach, Eger, and Neustadt without further incident. We approached the beautiful town of Regensburg as the sun rose; here there was traffic, much traffic, and many hitchhikers. We picked up as many as we could. Sometimes as many as ten people were jammed in the back of the truck. Comfort was no concern; the main object for these poor souls was to get the ride, to get that much closer to wherever they were going. Usually this was their last chance to get home or to some place equally important. At the Regensburg railroad station we dropped our thankful passengers, and stopped ourselves beyond Regensburg and rested. We found a spot a few hundred yards off the highway, near a little stream, where we could wash and freshen up, and the men could shave. Then we sprawled on the grass and ate some of the sandwiches, which we washed down with a delicious one-to-two mixture of Vermouth and spring water. It was idyllic, in sharp contrast to the horrors of the war from which we were fleeing.

For an hour we relaxed; then started again. Traffic was heavy and slowed us down quite a bit. *Jabos* were again a problem.

Progress was slow, and it was dark by the time we reached Augsburg. We dropped more hitchhikers at the Augsburg station, and continued on. Bombers made it dangerous to remain inside a big city overnight. Eventually, south of Landsberg-Lech, we pulled off the road and parked under some trees, there to await the morning. The elevation was only 2000 feet, but at that time of year it got pretty cold at night, and our stay was most uncomfortable. As a result, we were all up early in the morning. This day, we hoped to reach Oberammergau.

Then, without warning, our whole project hung in the balance. The truck would not start. This was, I think, the worst moment of the whole journey. A thousand thoughts flashed through my mind, all dominated by the one consideration: What would we do if the truck were through?

Minutes dragged by while we searched for the trouble. Finally we spotted a lot of water in the glass of the gasoline filter, emptied it, and dried it and the fuel lines. Then, I climbed in and tried the starter. The motor roared into life, and my heart soared. While the engine idled, Hans, Paul, and I cleaned up as much as possible, and then we resumed our journey.

Our route now took us along an easy, level road on the valley floor. Travel poster mountains towered in the background, and the meadows through which we passed were vividly green. Dark wooden farmhouses with balconies and long roofs almost touching the ground told us we were in Bavaria.

As we approached Oberammergau and the end of our expedition, we passed scattered herds of grazing cattle, and the tinkling of the big melodic Alpine bells was like music. At the edge of the village, we parked.

"Well," I said, turning to the others, "we made it."

We exchanged mutual congratulations. A sudden sense of relief swept over me, a kind of shock reaction to the terrifying realization of the adventure we had just had. When I said "we made it," it was with a sense, almost, of exhaustion.

"Wait here," I said after a moment's reflection. "I'll walk into town and see what the situation is."

I soon spotted familiar faces. One man, an engineer who had been with me on P-7, recognized me instantly.

"Where is everybody?" I exclaimed.

He spread his arms.

"All over the place. Hotels, restaurants, though some have

moved farther on." He shook his head sadly. "Nothing is prepared here. Quarters are scarce. Everything is disorganized."

Others I talked to gave me much the same picture. Morale was very low. Yet, how else could it be, living as we were in the company of complete disaster? Nobody really believed that actual work would ever be started again, nor had we believed it from the start of the move. Apparently, though, if only to keep busy, some groups were trying to set up improvised drafting tables and to establish offices. But there were no supplies, and there was certainly no hardware. The simple fact was that Germany was split asunder, crumbling; communications had virtually ceased; and the Allies were advancing at every point.

I was looking for von Braun. It was about noon when I finally found him in a small hotel at the other end of town. The lobby was swarming with SS men, sinister and menacing in their aspect. They were perhaps less arrogant than usual, but their mere presence was disquieting.

The moment von Braun spotted me, he came over and said, very quickly, "Wait in the lobby. I'll be with you in a minute."

Soon he emerged from a temporary office and walked me over to a reasonably private corner, and shook my hand.

"So you did make it." He smiled. "It's good to see you back. But we can't discuss your mission here. These fellows are"—he tossed his head in the direction of the SS-crowded lobby—"part of Kammler's gang, and I suspect they're up to no good. Just answer me this: Were you successful?"

"Yes," I answered simply.

"Ah!" He seemed profoundly relieved. "Good. All the more reason for us to clear out of here." He looked around again. "How did you get here?"

"In one of the trucks we used for the mission. But," I added hastily, "we're low on gas."

"Very well." He gripped my hand again. "Drive over to the south entrance to the village. I'll meet you there."

He walked back toward the office. I stared after him for a moment. I felt eyes upon me; it was an SS man in the corner.

I left the hotel, full of concern.

My companions pestered me to know what was happening,

but I could say little. I mentioned von Braun's concern over the presence of the SS men.

"Oh," said Hans, somewhat mollified.

When von Braun drove up beside the truck, Hans Lindenberg, one of the key men in thrust chamber development at Peenemünde, was with him. I went over to the window of their car.

Von Braun was just as enigmatic as he had been at the hotel. "There's an army depot at Ettal, just a short way from here," he said. "We'll go there and pick up a few things we'll need, and then go on to Weilheim for the night."

I introduced Irmel, Hans, and Paul, and explained their presence. Von Braun was his usual personable self. "Will you have enough gas?" he ventured. "You mentioned earlier—"

"Yes, I think so. Don't you, Hans?"

Hans nodded.

"Very well. Then follow us," von Braun said, and rolled up the window.

Ettal is a town famous for its monastery, which in turn is even better known for its fine, sweet liqueur. We hesitated only briefly at the depot there, and then swung north on an intersecting highway that took us, in a few hours, to Weilheim. It was already night when we arrived.

Von Braun's car pulled up in front of a *Behelfsheim,* a kind of emergency housing tract built by the government to replace homes destroyed in bombing raids on the big cities. They were small houses, designed for maximum utility, and not too mean, by comparison with some of the places in which I had lived during the war years.

Von Braun explained that he had been here since the move to Oberammergau. "Old friends," he smiled.

Magnus von Braun was there, and we exchanged warm greetings; it had been some time since we had seen each other. Meanwhile, the women spread a meal for us civilians. Hans and Paul had decided to go into town to eat.

"One moment!" I exclaimed as we were about to sit down for the meal. I was thinking about the case of Italian vermouth which we had been carrying all over central Germany, and in a moment I had fetched a couple of bottles. Soon, with the combination of candlelight—there being no electricity—Magnus' superb accordion playing, and the vermouth, a fine relaxed atmosphere developed. A feeling, a mood, was generated which I had not experienced for a long time. Looking back in retrospect upon that wonderful evening, it seems almost as though the sure knowledge of the impending end of everything freed us from our worries, at least for a while. So we relaxed and sang and drank a little. That night, we four travelers spent one last night in the truck which had seen us through so much.

15

DISSOCIATION

With morning came a return to the important matters at hand. We all gathered around von Braun for instructions. It was clear, to me at least, that he had a future in mind. He began with his evaluation of the *status quo*.

"You are aware of the presence of these SS men in Oberammergau," he said, somewhat grimly. "Frankly, I am unhappy about this. Regardless of what is happening to Germany, our personal technical knowledge, our knowledge of the hidden location of our research results—in these things, we are the bearers of an entire engineering science. I'm afraid these SS men may develop a *Totila* complex and try to destroy us and everything we've done." Now he leaned forward very tensely. "Rather than let this happen, rather than let us or our documents fall into their hands, I feel that we should leave this area. General Dornberger has already taken steps to this end, and has established himself and the remnants of his staff at *Haus Ingeborg,* in Oberjoch near the Adolf Hitler Pass. I propose that we join him. There will be a rather large number of people up there, more even than I think these frustrated SS men would care to tackle. I'm starting tomorrow."

There was of course no gainsaying the wisdom of his remarks. I certainly was not enthralled by the prospect of remaining in Oberammergau under the circumstances, and this seemed an opportunity to make my personal preparations for the arrival of our conquerors.

The next morning von Braun left and shortly after, I followed

181

in the truck, accompanied by Irmel, Hans, and Paul. I detoured through Pfronten, where I would be able to leave Irmel in the safe hands of some old family friends. Things were too much up in the air now; nobody knew what was going to happen next, and it seemed to me the only way.

We found a room for her there, and my friends promised they would help her all they could. I went about the business of getting her set up in the room as quickly as possible, and made my goodbyes sadly. There seemed so little time! I told her I would be back when I could manage it; I could hardly be more definite under the circumstances. It was with a most heavy heart that I left her and rejoined Hans and Paul in the truck for the trip up to the pass.

The day was almost gone by the time we got going, and after a tedious climbing drive up narrow mountain roads, it was long after dark when we finally arrived at Oberjoch. We could see houses and dim lights here and there, and there were people walking around. I pulled over and hailed one of them.

"How do we get to *Haus Ingeborg?*"

The man pointed.

"About two hundred yards over there."

I thanked him and drove up a steep access road into a parking area outside a large, three-story hotel with a sloping roof. We walked over to wide stairs, up through a heavy door, and found ourselves in a modern, brightly lit lobby. There were a number of people, many in German Army uniforms, present. I spotted Magnus almost immediately and walked over to him.

"I'll introduce you to Corporal Seidlitz, who's in charge of the rooms," he said. "We've an arrangement whereby he works through the owner of *Ingeborg.*"

In a few moments I had been assigned a single room on the second floor. It was rather well appointed, especially considering the times, and in the morning I discovered that it provided a magnificent view of the mountains. Hans and Paul were assigned rooms on the top floor.

This was April 15, 1945. History now begins to obtrude on my story, and exact dates begin to have a special significance. I think of the ultimate importance to me of May 2, and I have a vivid impression of the days flashing by like the pages on a calendar.

Thus, on April 15, late in the evening, I was nibbling a few sandwiches and thinking about events past and present. When my hunger had been satisfied, I went downstairs and began locating people I knew: Dornberger, Lt. Col. Axster of his staff, and then Bernhard Tessmann, who also had returned safely from the classified material operation. We exchanged intervening adventures.

I felt an intense need to relate the detailed story of the classified material mission to von Braun, and with Tessmann's assistance I located the two brothers. Tessmann, of course, had told him the meat of the story, but I wanted to fill in all the details. Magnus had not yet heard it in full, and the four of us were able to discuss various aspects of it pretty thoroughly.

My story told, exhaustion set in and I excused myself. I literally fell into bed, and with the help of that wonderful, fresh, spring mountain air I spent my first really comfortable night in many, many days.

The next seventy-two hours were without singular event, waiting. I hiked; got in some good reading; and also found some chess opponents. I hadn't played for quite a while and spent many hours at this. Meals, provided by the Army, were excellent. Somewhere down the mountain, beyond Hindelang, was a commissary; every day a truck was sent down to pick up our food.

Evenings were usually spent in the dining room, where we played chess or exchanged stories. Once in a while, a bunch of us would gather in von Braun's room, and the result was always a spirited evening marked by bright conversation. Inevitably there was benevolent bantering, and it didn't take us long to run through von Braun's stock of sweet vermouth.

After three days of this inactivity, I got my bicycle and rode down the hill to Pfronten to see how everything was working out for Irmel.

We spent a few delightful hours together, and then I had to make the depressing trip back. It was uphill all the way, and took me a couple of hours.

As I entered the hotel, the radio at the far end of the lobby was blaring an address by Josef Goebbels in honor of Hitler's birthday. I halted and listened. His words amazed me; it was simply fantastic how the man could ignore the facts and speak as though everything were just fine—a mere matter of days until the great miracle would happen. I reflected that we and our V-2 had once been that miracle—and what of us now? I shook my head and went on up to my room.

April 20, the following day, a little ceremony commemorating Hitler's 56th birthday was held in front of the hotel. It was a notably subdued affair. The Army officer who delivered the speech of the day was most skillful in his consideration of the realistic circumstances. I admired him for his approach, which differed so noticeably from Goebbels' of the night before.

Time moved, and the sense of helpless waiting heightened. Nature turned on us, in a sense; there was rain, and shortly, snow. This meant no more trips to Pfronten. Instead it meant more talking, anxious and wondering; more subdued chess playing; desperate reading; and waiting, waiting.

After a few days of this, my old friend Hartmut and his wife arrived at *Haus Ingeborg* in the company of one of his staff men, Lieutenant Heims, and his wife. This came as a complete surprise, and we had a fine reunion.

"Our original plan," he told me over *ersatzkaffee* and rolls, "was simply to wait at Bad Sachsa for the inevitable arrival of the Americans. But at the last minute my wife became frightened at the sight of the soldiers approaching across the field, and so we left. In great haste, I might add," he appended, smiling.

Their journey to *Ingeborg* had been about as wild and adventurous as my own. I told him my story.

The weather improved but the news became steadily worse. I managed to make a couple of more trips to see Irmel, but even this could not drive from my mind the same question that was nagging us all—when and by whom? The Americans or the French? On the highway a hundred yards below the hotel, we could see a constant stream of fleeing civilians and soldiers with mobile equipment of all kinds. This went on night and day. Where to? Nobody knew, and, as a matter of fact, these fleeing people themselves probably did not know.

April 27: Suddenly, like some mass hysteria, the need for *us* to flee swept through *Ingeborg*.

"Let's clear out of here. I know of a chalet, high up in the mountains." In the surge of excitement, an Army major was placed in charge of the removal action. "Tomorrow morning, early, we leave!"

But as cooler heads would have foreseen, the following morning brought only confusion, and very little action. It was not until the afternoon that, in disorganized groups, we began to drift up the mountain toward the *Iseler* chalet.

It was a primitive, overcrowded place, marked particularly by the lack of sobriety on the part of the officers. There was just no organization, no plan, no one in charge. This was disintegration and chaos, and it served to bring back to me a sense of proportion which in the excitement of the last twenty-four hours I had lost.

I stayed just long enough to grasp the over-all picture—no more than a few minutes—and then walked back toward *Ingeborg,* sorely regretting the laborious climb up to the *Iseler* chalet. Perhaps, I thought as I trudged along, perhaps I should go to Pfronten. But the report was that it was already in American hands.

I ran into Tessmann. He was equally disgusted with both himself and the whole abortive move, and after we compared notes he suggested:

"Why don't you move in with me at *Hochpass Haus?* There's a room available."

This sounded like a good idea to me. At least it would be a change. After I had established myself in these new quarters, I wandered back to *Haus Ingeborg* to take advantage of its facilities and to see who was still there. I found von Braun and Dornberger, among others, but already many faces were missing. I also found a growing nervousness, a kind of frustration that the inevitable didn't happen. Why had no one come? Why were we not already in Allied hands? Radio Berlin was pretty inaccurate in general, but even so it was quite clear that the American forces had long since passed us by, moving along the foothills north of us.

April 29: Von Braun accosted me in the lobby of *Ingeborg* and suggested that I return there. I was more than ready. It seemed a very good idea to be as close as possible to central authority now. The following day, after I had again moved my laundry bag and suitcase, the news flashed through the hotel that the French were coming. The certainty seemed to be that they would arrive the following day, moving up the pass from Hindelang.

"They are mainly Moroccan troops," exclaimed someone.

Of all my experiences, in the Army, at Peenemünde, fleeing through Germany, none so tragicomic as that which then transpired had ever occurred. Looking back over the safe distance of years, it seems almost hilarious; but at the time we were in the grip of hysteria and uncertainty.

Reports had it that the Moroccans were particularly fierce soldiers, and that under the influence of alcohol they were just plain murderous. These reports squeezed from a terrified hotel employee the painful confession that his employer had thousands of bottles of wine stocked in the cellar. Over the frantic protests of the proprietor, we checked. It was true. We were furious. All this time, the proprietor of *Haus Ingeborg* had steadfastly proclaimed that he had nothing on the premises but cider. Not only had he denied us this simple pleasure, but it was obvious he hoped to improve his own position with the occupation forces by the lever of this fine hoard of wine. Our fury was really aroused, though, by the fear that he had placed in the hands of the Moroccans the elixir which could transform them into our assassins.

We decided something had to be done with that wine, and tonight, before the Moroccans arrived. So we got all the available trucks ready, and dragooned every man, civilian or soldier, in the place, including the hotel employees—except the owner. We formed a human chain. Down this line, from hand to hand, the bottles were passed. Hundreds, thousands of them: we worked for hours, an utterly exhausting task. The labels that flashed through my hands were fantastic: Heidsieck, Veuve Cliquot, Ettaler, Cinzano, Liebfraumilch, Rüdesheimer. Here and there, someone would put a bottle aside for later reference. And still the bottles came! Out of the steel cabinets, through the heavy doors that had sealed the wine against changes of temperature, down the narrow corridors, up the steep stairway, out through the front entrance and into the dark and onto the waiting trucks. Some bottles, I clearly recall, had no corks by the time they got a little way down the line.

By two o'clock in the morning we had loaded and dispatched to a nearby military hospital some five thousand bottles of wine and liqueur. The hospital inmates had quite a good time for a few days, with some three bottles per customer, at no charge!

So passed the morning of May 1, and there came no French, no Americans, no change at all. It was a dull gray day, with some rain. In the afternoon, over the radio came the dire statement: "Stand by for an important announcement."

We all gathered around the receiver, silent and really afraid. This, I thought, must be it. Capitulation. Then, after a few moments of static:

"The Führer was killed yesterday, April 30, in combat in his headquarters in Berlin." The announcement was read in the most matter-of-fact possible tone of voice.

We all looked at one another. Nobody said much; it was something which, one way or another, was bound to happen. Nor was it even a symbol of defeat. Germany herself, demoralized, battered, and overrun, was that symbol. A little man, who had long since ceased to matter, had died. That was all. Gradually the crowd dispersed, some going to the dining room to finish interrupted meals, others back to their chess games or to their books. And we learned later, of course, that instead of being killed in combat, Hitler had actually committed suicide in his Berlin air raid bunker, along with his mistress, Eva Braun.

Early in the morning of the next day, May 2, Wernher von Braun summoned several of us to his room. He seemed more relaxed than for many days. I knew immediately that the waiting was over. He spoke simply, with real firmness:

"Magnus, who speaks English, has just left by bicycle to establish contact with the American forces at Reutte. We cannot wait here forever."

At two in the afternoon, Magnus returned. The arrangements with the Americans had been made. Wernher listened quietly to his report, then turned and ordered three BMW passenger cars to be readied with drivers.

Thus, in the dull, rainy, late afternoon of Wednesday, May 2, 1945, seven men in civilian clothes gradually assembled at the entrance to *Haus Ingeborg:* Dr. Wernher von Braun, engineering director and the driving spirit at Peenemünde where the rocket age was born; his brother Magnus, most recently engineer in charge of gyroscope mass production at *Mittelwerke;* General Dr. Walter Dornberger, the patron of German rocketry; Hans Lindenberg, mass production V-2 combustion chamber engineer; Bernhard Tessmann, chief designer of Peenemünde's test facilities; Lt. Col. Dr. Herbert Axster, an officer on Dornberger's staff; and myself.

Shortly, the fateful convoy of BMW's pulled up and we loaded the material we were taking with us, and then climbed in. We were all tightly jammed among an assortment of suitcases, trunks, briefcases, and boxes. I had the uneasy sensation that this was now all that remained of one of the greatest engineering adventures of modern times.

At last, we got underway, and the three field-gray cars began their lonely descent from the Adolf Hitler Pass toward the little Austrian village of Schattwald. This same road, that a few weeks before had carried an endless jumbled column of cars, trucks, horse carriages, pushcarts—the sad remnants of a scattered German Army—in confused flight toward a nonexistent mountain retreat, was empty of traffic save for our forlorn little convoy. The clouds were low and thick and, along with the densely wooded slopes of the Kuehgund mountains, cloaked us in somber solitude. Everyone was serious, thoughtful, silent. No one knew what the future held, either in the next few minutes in Schattwald, or in the days, months, and years that might follow.

The growl of the car's engine and the splash of rain, the absence of any sign of life created a sensation of detachment, of timeless, dimensionless space. Once again the immutable hand of fate seemed to be falling between me and the work I loved so much.

16

AS THE PHOENIX RISES...

Suddenly, around a curve, an American soldier came into view, and waved us to a stop. Magnus got out and briefly showed a piece of paper to the guard, who then motioned us all into a nearby building, which many years ago must have been an Austrian customs station.

Tense and apprehensive, we entered. There, other soldiers motioned us to sit down on chairs against a brick wall. Their attitude was correct, yet indifferent, and no conversation took place. An officer started a long series of telephone calls. I had had some English in high school, but I could hardly understand a word that was spoken.

After about half an hour, we were directed back to our cars and soon our convoy was on its way again. This time, however, we were flanked by two vehicles which I soon learned were "jeeps," and which I later got to know quite intimately and to admire, though I never completely understood the need for such complete lack of comfort.

We reached Reutte after dark, and stopped in front of a typical Bavarian-Austrian-style mansion. Electricity had not yet been restored, and the town was dark. We were directed into a large dimly lit hall inside the building. At one end was a table covered with papers, and lighted by a single candle. The face of a U.S. officer, sifting through the papers, was ghostlike in the semi-darkness.

Our small party gathered in irregular groups, our faces like masks in the dark. There were others already there, including a few officers from Dornberger's former staff, who must have been rounded up in some other manner.

Then U.S. personnel, speaking excellent German, started to record our names. There was little formality and, after only a short while, we were all assigned to small rooms in the spacious house. The rooms were not particularly tidy and the beds were not freshly made, to be sure, but no one cared. Everything that went on was so complete a change from our environment of only a few hours ago, that we didn't even notice. Suddenly, the electric lights went on. We could make out our individual luggage pieces, get toilet articles, wash, comb, and in general look a little more civilized. To our complete surprise, we were all led to a spacious dining room and treated to a simple but excellent meal, including fresh eggs, butter, and incredibly white bread, something we hadn't seen for many years. Several U.S. soldiers sat in the background, reading or listening to a radio. There was only limited conversation among ourselves. Without further event, we were all returned to our rooms and soon were soundly asleep.

The next morning was a pleasant, though still cold, early spring day. With only a few instructions, we were all led to a temporary building, containing an officers' mess, and an American-style breakfast. The effect of this meal on us after five war years was tremendous. I felt almost uncomfortable. The absolutely correct treatment that we had been given so far was a great relief.

When we emerged from the mess hall, several Army photographers were on hand and spent some time taking pictures of our group and several of the individuals, notably von Braun. Then we returned to our quarters. Several hours went by in small talk and reading. I used the time to take some notes. Then, without our knowing what was going to happen, we were told to pick up our luggage and board an open U.S. Army truck in front of the house. I noticed immediately that Wernher von Braun and Dornberger were missing.

Then, after hours of driving, we stopped in front of a school building in the little town of Peiting. As we unloaded, we found ourselves unexpectedly surrounded by old friends. There was Kaschig from P-7, Scharnowski, Hueter, and many of the others.

Slowly, under these strange circumstances, the people of Peene-münde were being reassembled. I thought, almost afraid to be hopeful, of that legendary bird of Egypt, the Phoenix, that arose from the ashes of the fire that consumed it.

Inside the school building, we were in for another surprise. It was the town kindergarten, and the furniture and sanitary instal-lations were scaled accordingly. Even with no usable furniture, no beds, not even a rug, we spent a joyful and interesting evening of storytelling by candlelight. I still had a bottle of sweet ver-mouth in my suitcase, which was just enough for a sip for every-body. The night on the bare floor reminded me of my nights in the air raid shelter in Berlin.

Nothing happened during the following days. From time to time rumors of departure flared up, then turned out to be false alarms. Our movements were limited, but visits to a nearby inn for meals were permitted. One day, unexpectedly, Hartmut's wife, Waltraut, showed up. She was frantic. Hartmut had been arrested by U.S. military authorities, upon denunciation of villagers who thought he was a member of Himmler's SS troops. It later turned out that others had similar temporary fates, but all were soon exonerated of that charge. Then, a few days later, we were on the go again. Trucks pulled up and luggage was loaded.

This trip lasted several hours. Again the countryside we passed through was quite familiar: Oberammergau, Ettal, and finally Garmisch-Partenkirchen, the latter a clean, well-to-do resort area which had gained fame as the site of the 1936 winter Olympics. The trucks finally came to a halt in the courtyard of a huge former German military administration building. There were sev-eral hundred other Peenemünde men to greet us, many of them close associates. We were told that the third story of the building still had several empty rooms, and we immediately started moving in and making them as comfortable as possible. Fortunately, cots and lockers were amply available in the basement, and before long we were all fairly comfortably established. Once again, the in-evitable exchange of stories ranged far into the late night. The *Stabsgebaeude,* Staff Building, was to be my home for close to three months. More former Peenemünders continued to drift in until finally a little over four hundred people were held in the staff building. Among those coming in late were Hartmut and his wife. He was one of the very few who had succeeded in staying with his wife throughout this period.

Looking back, these months in Garmisch do not register as outright dreadful prison times. Only the inability to communicate with our families and loved ones, due to the complete absence of a mail or telephone system for many months, really bothered us. Otherwise, the staff building and its courtyard were large enough to relieve the feeling of narrow confinement. The view from the windows in all directions was beautiful, breathtaking at times, with Germany's highest peak, the Zugspitze, in plain view. The season was just right: mountain springtime. Trees by now had donned their fresh, new green; flowers were everywhere as far as one could see from our windows and balconies. Rain was infrequent, and almost every day sunbathing was possible in the lawn-covered yard. Frequently, on such days, I went to the attic and out onto the roof, enjoying a superb, unrestricted mountain view in all directions.

Within our boundaries there were no further restrictions, save a few self-imposed house rules. Food for a short while was supplied in the form of U.S. Army K-rations. Then the newly appointed German authorities took over the supply. Neither form was extravagant, but adequate. There were ample kitchen and mess hall facilities in the basement. There even were hospital facilities on the first floor. Soon our group of highly trained people set out to organize activities to keep the mind busy and the time spent purposeful. There were lecture series in technical fields at the university level: thermodynamics, astronomy, nuclear physics, mathematics, ballistics, meteorology, guidance, and several other topics, even the art of chess playing, followed in due course by the inevitable chess tournament.

There was an excellent library. A small orchestra soon formed and gave modest evening concerts in the auditorium located in the center of the building. A theatrical group was formed which eventually "produced" four plays, to which everyone had to bring his own chair.

As one might expect, confinement of over four hundred people in an area totaling no more than a few acres would not be entirely without problems. However, all things considered, the period went by with exceptional smoothness. Lt. Col. John O'Mara was in charge as the representative of the U.S. authorities. He was ably assisted by his aide, Lt. Fox, and by others whose names I do not remember. During the earlier weeks, it was only natural that Wernher von Braun would be the head and spokesman for the German group. When he was transferred to another location, Dornberger took over until he, too, disappeared. Other men followed as spokesmen at one time or another. Dr. Netzer of the Peenemünde guidance department was the last of them, until the Garmisch Camp was finally dissolved.

Many of these little problems were resolved in mass meetings with all inhabitants participating. Here, pros and cons were aired, and decisions were made by hand-raising in a quickly adopted, remarkably democratic fashion. Here, we also established certain basic operating procedures: evening quiet hours; a code of ethics; whether we would have soup for breakfast, etc. These meetings, *Hauptversammlungen,* were to be a stock in trade with the German group for several years to come. The meetings were addressed by the German and the U.S. spokesmen alike, and they affected, more than any other single factor, the attitude, the feelings, the emotions, the willingness to cooperate, and the decisions made by the group as well as by individuals of this German rocket specialist group.

More than anything else at Garmisch, however, we had time to think and talk. There was no work, no deadline, nor did we appear to be going anywhere any time soon. For many of us it was the first time in months, maybe years, we had had the opportunity to sit down and calmly, casually contemplate the past, take stock of the present, and speculate on our future.

Peenemünde was no more. The *Wunder-Waffen* had not brought victory out of defeat. We thought back over our reactions at that time, on the evening of September 8, 1944, in particular, when we heard that the first V-2 had been launched against England. Almost to a man, I feel, this was to us a confirmation of a tough engineering job well done, rather than a military victory. All of us knew deep in our hearts that by then the war was too far gone for the A-4 to materially alter the grinding course of history.

Then too, in the scenic splendor of Garmisch, we realized that there had been a kind of detachment at Peenemünde. The war wasn't real. It was a nuisance somewhere else, a devil conjured up to make an already tough technological task all the more impossible, and which only occasionally brought its wrath down on us. What were real were the day-to-day tasks and the long term engineering goal toward which we built. Looking back from now, 1962, I realize that the Peenemünde engineer's view of the V-2 was little different from the Convair engineer's view of the Atlas, or the Douglas engineer's view of the Thor today.

Talk turned often to the future of rocketry in peacetime. Would the funds be made available for the peaceful exploration of space in a volume comparable to that spent on developing rockets for death and destruction? And who would do it, which country or countries? This inevitably brought the conversation around to ourselves, for we with our experience and our cache of technical data were the only major source of large rocket know-how in the world.

Throughout the early days in this Bavarian resort town, guards would occasionally drop hints about "our being in America in a few weeks." This raised all kinds of speculation about the future, and also served to dispel one early fear voiced by some: that we were being held pending political or other—war crimes was a term we heard with dismay—prosecutions. Simultaneously rumors became persistent that German industry would be dismantled and removed. The prospect was not very encouraging to a professional engineer.

The rumors about "going to America" really gained impetus after one of Col. O'Mara's trips to USFET at Frankfurt am Main —on May 31, 1945 to be exact. Quickly we overthought and overtalked these rumors into "imminent prospects." My concern ranged from "What would I do about Irmel, my family?" to the conceivable prospect of changing our citizenships—a wholly new thought. I remember distinctly that this came up in a conversation with Hartmut one afternoon on the lawn at Garmisch, and that we discussed it in a matter-of-fact way, like people in a crippled airplane who have just narrowly escaped disaster, and who find no difficulty whatsoever in throwing overboard what under normal circumstances they would not part with under any conditions.

The matter-of-factness with which we were able to discuss the possibility, in fact the desirability, of a change of citizenship—which only a few years earlier would have been unthinkable—made me ponder on the extremes to which circumstances had brought us. Looking back on those days, I cannot see that my, and the group's, acceptance of this possibility was basically any different from most other emigrations in the past centuries. Did we expect to evade unfavorable conditions at home and hope to find, through work, personal improvement abroad? The man that denied that this was a factor would be dishonest. Was this not the prime motivation of most emigrations? Nor was it solely the chance to continue work on big rockets. Would any of us have refused to go to America if we had been told first that we would not be allowed to continue in rocketry? We might have thought a little longer, but in the end most of us, I am sure, would have made the move. I did not believe then, nor do I believe now that rocket specialists—any more than any other kind of specialist—should be fanatics who abandon family and home and country for the sole reason of rocketry. Again, we were not "superengineers." We were human beings.

From time to time, groups or individuals departed in various directions to pick up missing baggage or personnel at Oberjoch, or to unknown locations in connection with release from German military status. Some of those departing returned after a while; others didn't. Whenever I learned of such trips, and that was mostly on very short notice, I grabbed long-prepared letters and packets and rushed down to the lobby in the hope that the travelers might pass through the village where I had left Irmel, or that they somehow might get word to my parents in northern Germany. But I did not succeed until a long time later. Gradually, however, our uneasiness grew. Questions were raised as to why we were still being held there. Our political backgrounds had been investigated, and no reason had been found for any action; nowhere were civilians in western Germany subject to such restrictions as ours.

Lt. Col. O'Mara did what he could to clarify matters. Finally his repeated trips to the USFET headquarters at Frankfurt am Main brought some action. First, a small group of persons having their homes in the Russian occupied zone were screened and released. Somewhat later, a larger group of predominantly non-technical people in military status were alerted and soon left for a separation camp. But there still was no word regarding the specialists. Unexpectedly, in mid-June, a mass meeting was called. A U.S. officer briefly announced that the possibility existed for us to continue rocket work in the United States. Willingness to conduct such work was to be expressed by signature on a short slip of paper, which he quickly distributed. The paper did not mention any conditions under which such work would be conducted, and the officer was not in a position to supply further details other than that the signature would have to be executed without any conditions specified. When the several hundred slips were collected, only six individuals had signed, none of whom I knew.

One sunny morning, shortly before his permanent departure from Garmisch, Dornberger came to the lawn and called me aside. "You and I may shortly have to start a trip north."

My ears perked up.

"Will we have an opportunity to pass through Pfronten and see Irmel, and get some mail to my parents?" was my immediate reaction.

"I don't know," Dornberger answered. "Our trip is in connection with the classified material you have hidden in the Harz Mountains. I think you will have to reveal the location, particularly since the demarcation line between the Western and Eastern Zones of Occupation is still not frozen. You have to show us exactly where the material is."

I could only agree. If, as the indications seemed to be, continuation of our work would be possible some day, then availability of these documents would probably save us several years of tedious and painstaking reconstruction work.

"I can be ready to leave in less than an hour," I told Dornberger, and went to my room for some preparatory measures. However, day after day passed by without any further word regarding our mission. Then, weeks later, Dornberger said:

"It seems our trip will not come about. I'm not entirely certain what happened, but it seems the material has been located already."

I could not hide my disappointment. Not only had I expected a much closer contact with the activities we all hoped would lead to a working agreement, but at the same time I had counted on a possibility of making contact with Irmel. I had to admit to myself that, truly, I had never believed that my acting as a guide was absolutely necessary, because I had disclosed the hiding place to Wernher von Braun and Karl Otto Fleischer, as instructed, right after that mission had been completed.

Later, in the early afternoon of July 21, 1945, a special meeting was called, where it was announced that a selected group would be surrendered to the British to conduct specific work. On the second day after, at 9 a.m., everybody listed was to report ready to leave, with all his luggage prepared for loading onto trucks and subsequent transportation north. My name was among those listed. By the time next morning rolled around, I wasn't about to go. Working for the British was a completely new thought. Sparse rumors that had reached us concerning the British ranged over a wide scale, from reports of being the fairest, to the exact contrary, in which Montgomery's arrogance often figured. That the British attitude toward the V-2 specialists might be anything but broadminded appeared to be a logical conclusion. But more importantly, how would I ever know what had happened to Irmel, or to my parents? I was determined to stay here. Nothing would be gained from formal applications to that effect. I had to "forget" the hour of departure and stay out of sight.

Early next morning, I saw the trucks pull into the side road on to which the yard opened. As my window faced the opposite direction, I could only guess what was going on in the forecourt. There was not a sound inside the building. I pictured people clambering up truck gates and settling onto benches as comfortably as possible for the long journey, and the others bidding them bon voyage. I felt quite alone. Suddenly the calm of the building was interrupted by the clatter of footsteps reverberating through the corridors. Different voices shouted my name from various parts of the building. Door handles were pulled, doors slammed again. The striding tromp of boots stamped methodically down my hall, I heard room doors open and slam, closer and closer.

"Herr Huzel! Dieter Huzel!" One voice grew sharply louder than the others.

Suddenly, it was in the next room.

"Herr Huzel?" The door slammed.

I flattened against the wall of my room behind the door—an old ploy, but I couldn't see myself hiding under a bed!

Sharply, the door to my room swung open, stopping only a fraction of an inch from my chest. The soldier hurriedly surveyed the room and was gone. I breathed again. Would they, I wondered, have dragged me kicking and screaming to the trucks, like a little boy on his reluctant way to the dentist? The simile made me laugh.

One by one the voices faded and disappeared, and soon the building was silent again. Shortly, I heard the muffled noise of truck engines being started and, peering carefully around the edge of a window, I saw the trucks pull onto the main road and disappear in the distance. Quickly, the routine noises of those who remained spread throughout the building.

In the afternoon, Hartmut's roommate, who knew of my plan, came in and told me that everything was quiet. By now the trucks were beyond reach of a quickly-dispatched jeep. I asked him to inform Dr. Netzer, our *Hauptversammlungen* spokesman, of my whereabouts, and it wasn't long before he was in to see me. Initially, of course, he was not very happy. I explained my motives to him and my desire to cause as little embarrassment as possible to all concerned. I asked him to convey this to Col. O'Mara, who would probably be most interested to know that no one was really missing.

The matter was subsequently resolved quietly between Col. O'Mara and myself. He promised to see to it personally that my messages, which I had tried to send out for months, would be dispatched. In return I agreed to follow the British group at the next opportunity.

During the following days, the building rapidly emptied until I was one of the last three or four people left. On July 31, 1945, Col. O'Mara advised me that no transportation north had come along so far. By now I knew that "north" meant the German North Sea shore town of Cuxhaven, where British activities with

V-2 rocket material were reported. As the staff building was soon to be surrendered to some other unit, Col. O'Mara invited me to live in his house until my trip north. Within less than an hour, I had my things transferred to a spacious house a few blocks away. Not only did I find there the most excellent of food, but also I was permitted for the first time in months to move freely about town, with the promise not to go beyond a certain distance. A few days later, I received a letter from Irmel, telling me that all was well, and a great worry was lifted from my mind.

Once I had agreed to cooperate, I wanted to see the Cuxhaven assignment completed as expeditiously as possible. A few days after my move from the staff building, Col. O'Mara's group packed and departed. I was handed over to an MP unit and, for the first time, found myself truly a prisoner.

After weeks, finally, a British light truck pulled up under the command of a 'Leftenant' Goffey to take me north.

We were waiting in the Garmisch market place for some paper-work to be cleared up, when suddenly my mother stood in front of me. She had heard about our group being retained at Garmisch. She had come all the way—by flagging down trucks, by short train rides, but mostly, however, in box cars—from my almost completely destroyed home town of Essen on the Ruhr. It was a joyous reunion. I learned happily that both she and my father had gotten through the last fighting there all right, and that both were in fair condition, although father seemed to suffer considerably from the complete loss of everything he had worked for during his life, and was unable to do anything about it, now that he was almost 70. I left my best wishes with her and the promise to communicate whenever and wherever the possibility would present itself. Then the truck was on its way, only to run smack into a tree the next day, causing a layover somewhere in central Germany for several days, until a replacement truck had been sent out from Cuxhaven. Finally, in the late evening of August 12, 1945, I passed through the gates of the British camp at Altenwalde near Cuxhaven. Like the Phoenix . . . I thought again, as I rejoined many of those from Peenemünde and found myself again working with rockets.

17

OPERATION BACKFIRE

Utilizing the hangars and other facilities of the former German Navy Artillery Range at Altenwalde, the British had initiated what was to become known as "Operation Backfire." Somewhat ironically, it might be described as an effort to become familiar with the other end of a trajectory. Technically, this operation resulted in one of the most comprehensive evaluations of the V-2 weapons system ever attempted. In fact, the full meaning and understanding of the fact that in addition to the missile itself, at least as much equipment is also needed to prepare it for flight was formulated here, probably for the first time. The resulting extensive reports on Operation Backfire, both in writing and in the form of motion pictures, were more comprehensive than anything that existed in German files. There were reasons for this. German security provisions during wartime would never have permitted such a broad coverage, in accordance with the ruling that no one was to know more about the entire system than the absolute minimum required for his own work. Furthermore, there had simply not been enough time and manpower available to attempt such an undertaking.

The British Operation Backfire was designed simply to completely evaluate the entire V-2 system, interrogate German personnel specialized in all phases and subsystems of it, and then actually launch several missiles across the North Sea.

British treatment of the German group—which at this location included a complete military V-2 unit, enlisted men, technicians, and officers—was generous.

Once again, I was surrounded by familiar faces. Hans Lindenberg, who had been in the small group surrendering with von Braun at Schattwald, was the spokesman of the German civilian specialist team. He had been having relatively little trouble. After months of inactivity, everybody was happy to be working again in his chosen field. The fact that everything was purely for a technical show and unconnected to any military purpose, also contributed to the feelings of the men who realized that nowhere in those days would they have been able to feed themselves as well, find shelter, or work on as interesting a subject as here. Our only worry concerned the uncertainty of our long-range future. And there was, of course, our impatience to be done with these purely temporary tasks, to begin again to build a life, and to be rejoined with our loved ones.

When I arrived at what was known locally as "Camp A," there were relatively few functions connected with the analysis, and the launchings were amply staffed. The British Command, therefore, transferred me to "Camp C," a few miles away. Spokesman of the small German group here was Dr. Kurt Debus, who had succeeded me on P-7. There, too, I finally ran into Hartmut again. I found myself in a small group of no more than 15 or 20 men, who had been skimmed off, like myself, ostensibly to put down on paper what they thought was noteworthy of their activities at Peenemünde. Most of the time we were left with nearly nothing to do. The British man in charge at Camp C, a Mr. Stratford, gave me the job of describing the facilities at Test Stand P-7.

Thus, as in Garmisch, another period of chess playing, of discussions, and above all, of reading began. The custody procedures were handled extremely leniently. German prisoners of war were the unarmed guards and we had frequent permission to go into the nearby hamlet of Brockeswalde, or even farther away, into Cuxhaven, where a movie theatre had recently reopened, and a small library was available. In the opposite direction, a beach was less than an hour's walk away. Under other circumstances this would have been a nice way to spend the summer: a few months in the Alps, then a few more in the countryside near a beach—with all the time imaginable to read, study, or play. As it was, no one really enjoyed that period. We all wanted an end of it. There were still no mail connections, yet we often had disturbing news, particularly from the eastern provinces.

From time to time, we met with those from Camp A. We learned that preparations for several V-2 launchings were coming along well. Occasionally, rumors came through of the negotiations with U.S. authorities at Witzenhausen. But these were rumors only and did little to allay the anxieties that inevitably develop in even the most lenient confinement. However, it soon became an accepted fact that a select group of us would be transferred to the U.S., and in some manner continue work in the field of rocketry. How many, who, under what conditions, and for how long remained a complete mystery among our group at Cuxhaven.

One day, from somewhere, Hans Lindenberg received a list of over a hundred names, labeled "List One," of people that were to be offered a U.S. contract. My name was on it. I was elated. A few days later, however, I learned that several of those on the list, including myself, were merely "spares." Still later, from another "report," I got the impression that everything was completely up in the air again, and that I had better not count on anything.

Then, on September 6, I received two letters through a messenger, only a little over a week old. One was from Bernhard Tessmann, who had hidden the files with me. It contained a complete list of names, which later proved to be most accurate. My name was on it. At the bottom, there was a brief note, "For goodness sake, no more escapades now!"

The other was from Wernher von Braun:

Dear Mr. Huzel:

As you may have already been informed at Cuxhaven, your name is on List 1. Your expressed interest, but particularly your extensive experience in large rocket testing, have influenced this decision.

May I take this opportunity to point out that the term "dependents" in connection with certain rights in the forthcoming work contracts, does not include fiancées. If your previously expressed intentions to marry are as serious as I obtained the impression they are, I would like to urge you to make the matter legal prior to your departure.

Expecting to see you as a well-established husband in America, I remain with best regards

Sincerely yours,
W. v. Braun

Suddenly, everything brightened. Waiting became less strenuous; plans for all the things I wanted to do before I left made much more sense now; reading, including some English grammar, became more selected. Hartmut's name was on another "List 2" of additional personnel who might be called at a later date. We assured each other that rocket activity "over there" would grow rapidly and that he would soon be called. And soon there were lengthy discussions about when we would be released from Operation Backfire; then what would our assignments be, etc. I wondered if there would be enough time to spend a few days with my parents? Was Irmel still in Bavaria? Or had she given up and moved through the Eastern Zone to Berlin? How were negotiations coming along? Supposing I missed the boat?

On October 2, 1945, the first British-directed launching took place across the Baltic. It was a complete success. We in Camp C had been informed of the launch time. From a clearing near our quarters, we could clearly see the rocket rising, almost exactly on the predicted hour. Only two days later, the second launch went off, equally successful, as far as we could see. Later, reports indicated, though, that full range had not been achieved. On October 15, 1945, the third and final V-2 Operation Backfire launching took place, with no significant difficulties.

With the last item of the British effort successfully accomplished, everybody, including the British, started talking about and preparing for departure. Procedures got underway to supply final military release papers to those who needed them, obtain *Kennkarten,* Identification Cards, from the German authorities, and have the luggage inspected.

I received a special card:

Recommendation
Name: Dieter Huzel
Profession: Dipl. Ing.

The above named person has worked satisfactorily in cooperation with the British Military Authorities for the last three to four months, on a project which has now been completed. The bearer, who, during the project, was unable to apply for a post, is now available to be employed under the Allied Authorities in his technical capacity. His military career and political record have been investigated, and, in view of his recent good service, his re-employment is recommended.

21 October 1945
Headquarters
307 Inf. Bde

In a separate letter, Hans Lindenberg formally released me from the German employment ties, to whatever degree they still had existed.

On October 22, 1945, all the occupants of Camp C were transferred to Camp A. The next day, the first groups, mainly those who wanted to return to their former civilian occupations, left forever. On October 25, along with twelve others named in List 1, I left the Cuxhaven area by U.S. Military plane for Munich.

Shortly after we arrived at Munich, a U.S. Army truck picked us up and took us to the provincial town of Landshut on the Isar River, 40 miles away. Solidly built former German army barracks and their noncommissioned quarters, had been selected by the U.S. authorities to house the rocket specialist group and their families. It was nicknamed Camp Overcast. For many years, these quarters remained the shelters for dependent families of many of those departing.

One of my first steps was to reserve the right to one of the small apartments, which I would have to share with another family. The condition for the right to live there, rather than in a dormitory, was that I would have a family of my own, a wife. My immediate project was to get travel papers to Pfronten.

Col. Glazer, in charge of the housing project and his aide, Capt. Jones, were both very understanding, cooperative people. In the following weeks and months, I had ample opportunity to admire the patience of these men, who had to deal with a group which eventually, after the departure of the men, was almost entirely composed of women, among them several rival queens.

Within two days after my arrival, I had my simple paper:

CERTIFICATE

Landshut, 29 October 1945

Mr. Dieter Huzel is authorized to use the railway for a trip to Pfronten/Allgaeu and to come back with his wife.

/s/ Plummer F. Jones, Jr.
Capt. Hq. 3rd Army G-5 Section
Commander

18

MARRIAGE AND
SEPARATION

My arrival at Landshut and my efforts to obtain travel papers had coincided with the preparations for imminent departure of a major portion of the group of specialists selected for work in the U.S.—sixty-seven people in all. Wernher von Braun had left some time earlier, with a group of six other men for advance discussions and other preparations. I was anxious to get on with my own trip to meet Irmel as soon as possible.

It took me almost two days to cover the 125 miles to Pfronten. It was early afternoon when I took off from the Landshut railroad station, one of the very few buildings in this town which had been destroyed during the last days of fighting. Lovely Germany was cut and torn and painful to behold. The cities were hit the worst. In contrast, whole sections of the countryside showed no surface scars of the war. The people, however, had not recovered, and had not begun to fight their way back to civilization. When the slow, run-down train finally reached Munich, at an average speed of less than 20 miles per hour, the last connecting train had already left, and I had to spend the night on the cold floor of a former air raid shelter. Munich was still in rubble, and no hotels were available. The following day, I continued my journey, first by rail, then by lifts on trucks, then by train again. I walked the last eight miles, finally reaching Pfronten at dusk.

There was a joyful reunion with Irmel. We started making our plans the same evening. Within a few days, we had all the papers and licenses required for our marriage. In a very unassuming civil ceremony in the office of the Pfronten *Bürgermeister,* we were married on November 3, 1945. The same afternoon, we started our trip back to Landshut.

The first lap to Kempten was relatively easy. The next train from there to Augsburg was severely crowded, and we had some difficulty getting all our luggage into it. It was evening when we arrived. Next connection to Munich: 3:30 a.m.! The station was milling with people; lost souls months after the war's formal end, trying still "to get back." Apparently half the nation was on the move: chaos, poverty, and despair in desperate teeming motion.

Augsburg had suffered considerably. In the sparse illumination outside the station, we saw the disheartening silhouettes of gutted buildings in every direction. It was uncomfortably cold. Nearby, a sign announced *Wärmehalle,* Warm-up Room, and *Getränke,* Beverages. I peered briefly into the dense blue haze at the mass of humanity inside, and staggered out, half suffocated.

Irmel and I found and elbowed our way into a few spare feet underneath a closed ticket window in the station. Traffic at the neighboring windows was still going on. All night, without any letup, people streamed in and out of the drafty, cold hall. A constant din filled the air, doors slammed incessantly, and cold crept through our top coats from the concrete floor on which we sat. Occasionally one or the other of us would doze fitfully. It was unpleasant in the extreme, but for all that it was also wonderful. With Irmel's dark curls in disarray over the shoulder of my coat, I could think of only one thing. We were together, married, and a whole new and exciting future lay before us.

Many long and exhausting hours later we arrived at Camp Overcast. As soon as we were rested we started making our little room as livable as possible. Life in the camp had become considerably more quiet. The large group, referred to as "Shipment 1" by most, had left while I had been away. Another group, however, was already in preparation. Lists were being made, medical checkups arranged for, vaccinations obtained and certified, general instructions passed around. Once again, I found myself working with Hans Lindenberg, who had assumed the role of spokesman in support of a hired permanent administrator for the camp.

The next shipment was scheduled for late November. Before I left I wanted to see my parents again. At first I feared I would not have time. Then I ran head-on into another difficulty: "A trip to Essen? Why, that's in the British Zone. Let's see, Essen, in the Ruhr district: Prohibited Area, no travel allowed there until further notice. Sorry, nothing we can do about it."

I hastened from one department to another—German as well as U.S.—in vain. Then I had an idea. I applied for travel authorization to Frankfurt am Main, far north in the U.S. Zone. Permission was immediately obtained. My travel paper turned out to be a standard form:

Landshut, 10 Nov. 1945

Office of the Chief Ordnance Officer
    Headquarters USFET
        U.S. Army

Subject: Movement of German Civilians
To: Military Government Officer concerned

The bearer Mr. Huzel is a member of a group of scientists who have been evacuated and detained by War Department Order. They are permitted to move anywhere in the American zone for practicing their profession and getting a lodging and must register with the Military Government at destination. If it is necessary to contact this man, this office will do so through Military Government at his destination.

This office desires the bearer's presence in the American zone for an indefinite period of time.

R. W. Henns
2nd Lt. Ord. Dept.

The journey to Frankfurt was what I would call by now routine. The train to Munich was two hours late. I would have missed the connecting train, had that not been three hours late. Even then, it was so crowded I had to climb in the window.

At Frankfurt I had no trouble getting a ticket to Essen. In a few hours, I was in Giessen, only to learn that my connection was a "Daily, except Sunday" and Sunday it was, naturally. I hastily took a train to Kassel, which left in a few minutes. Later, at Kassel, the only connection was in the late evening, to Hannover, considerably more of a detour than I had intended. Moreover, the train was labeled "Restricted; Special Permit Required. No boarding at Kassel," on the billboard. In recent years, I had learned many ways to keep moving on the railroad. When in the Army, and particularly on those Kessler-engineered trips home from Russia, my education in this field had been well rounded.

A first ground rule is never to leave the platform if re-entry is questionable. A second: Stay out of sight. At Kassel, things were easy. Several passenger cars had been left standing at a far platform. I simply moved in, stretched out on a seat and took it easy. There were several hours to go until the "Restricted" would pull in. The next problem would be to get on board, despite the huge crowds trying to do the same, and the possibility of a "special pass" check. I solved this by waiting on the neighboring rather than the correct platform and sneaking in the side of the train. Thus, hours later, I was on my way to Hannover. Connection there was within an hour, by way of a train composed of box cars, the latter converted to passenger cars simply by labeling them as such.

Reunion with my parents and sisters was joyful, yet melancholy. Our house was no more and my parents lived with another family in their undestroyed house in the outskirts of Essen. I spent several days with them; we visited other relatives together, and I looked up my old schoolteacher. Otherwise there was little to see but rubble and debris wherever one stepped. Finally, on a clear, sunny afternoon in mid-November, I said goodbye to my parents and sisters. This was the last time I saw my father, for less than a year later, while I was far away, he died.

The trip back to Landshut was as adventurous as had been the journey in the opposite direction. In fact, going was so rough that I was unable to prevent the loss of almost a day, despite the use of every trick I knew. As a result, I missed the registration deadline for the second shipment by just one day. Although it was difficult to see why this postponed my departure, since that group of 21 people did not leave until ten days later, I was not too unhappy about it. It gave me a few quiet weeks with Irmel and we were able to spend Christmas together.

Hans Lindenberg, leaving with this second shipment on November 27, 1945, handed over his responsibilities to me. The latter were varied in nature, mostly trifling and sometimes unpleasant: to help distribute the few available furniture pieces; to find out the addresses and whereabouts of former Peenemünde people; to receive the applications of visitors hoping to participate in the U.S. work; to listen to complaints of the wives of those departed about the administrator, and to the administrator's complaints about the wives; to attend meetings with all the women or with the women's council, all abounding with questions, requests, complaints, applications for dismissal, votes of confidence, vetos, high pitched voices.

Shortly after New Year's, the departure date for the next group, Shipment 3, was set for January 11. In addition to the ten or twelve men already waiting in the camp, another dozen or so arrived from their home towns to join the group. Among them were Dr. Lippisch and my good friend from the guidance group at Test Stand 7, Dr. Ernst Stuhlinger. The remaining days passed quickly with no excitement, as everything had been prepared for so long. On the afternoon of Friday, January 11, 1946, our group boarded a special car in the train to Munich. Our luggage was quickly stored. Once on board I leaned out the window. Irmel looked up and pressed my hand. We exchanged some of that little nonsense and those trivia that always seem to come to mind at railroad stations. A picture flashed through my mind: only so recently my last departure from Berlin to Russia. But this time I was leaving my wife behind, and the odds of seeing each other again were vastly better. Then the engine jerked and the train pulled out slowly. We leaned out the windows, waving to our relatives. I could still see Irmel for a long while until she finally appeared lost in the crowd. Then I watched the general flutter of white handkerchiefs until these, too, disappeared in the distance.

As we settled back on our seats, someone said, "And now we are on our way to America." For a long while there was silence, each of us following his own thoughts and staring absently out the window.

19

OPERATION PAPERCLIP

In a sense, we arrived in America only two hours later. When, with exhausted puffing, our train from Landshut came to a final stop at the Munich main station, we transferred our luggage to a U.S. Army truck, which swiftly transferred us to the "Hotel America," a transient center for U.S. soldiers, passing through to and from the U.S. and all corners of the European Theater. It had formerly been an administration building or a school. Dormitories had been set up in the upper stories. The basement contained a cafeteria, where we obtained a simple, tasty meal, entirely novel in composition but thoroughly relished by all. The place was filled with U.S. soldiers of all branches engaged in lively conversation. The inadequacies of my school English were evident. A loudspeaker system inside and outside the building blared music without letup, the composition of which was as novel to us as had been that of the meal, although we may not always have relished it as much.

Our "troop leader" and "chaperone" was 1st Lt. Enno Hobbing, who spoke flawless German well seasoned with slang expressions. Early next morning he aroused us from our GI cots. Following a rich breakfast, we boarded an express train to Paris, on our way to Le Havre on the Atlantic coast. At Paris' Gare de l'Est Lt. Hobbing tried to get our car switched to Gare St. Lazare, to be attached to a suitable train going farther west. Fortunately, he failed. This gave us an opportunity, when riding back and forth in buses between railroad stations and U.S. provi-

212

sioning centers, to see a little of the lovely and completely un-harmed city, which I myself had not visited before.

After one week in Le Havre at "Fort Home Run"—an old World War I fortress transformed into another U.S. transient center—we picked up our luggage once more and boarded the Liberty ship, "Central Falls." On January 21, 1946, we sailed for New York. As the coast of Europe faded in the distance and our raucous escort of careening, screaming seagulls one by one wheeled and headed back to land, thoughts and questions tumbled through my mind—thoughts and questions that could only be confirmed and answered in the land and future that lay across the sea.

Early on the morning of February 3, 1946, the lights of New York came into sight. I had risen quite early, not to miss any-thing. There were a few others on deck, including a few American soldiers. They pointed out landmarks I had heard about so often, but had never seen, the lights of the Shore Parkway, the Statue of Liberty, Staten Island, and, as we passed the narrowest point between the shores, a whole glittering panorama of lights. Sud-denly, there was activity on the water all around us. Ferries several stories high, ablaze with lights, criss-crossed the bay waters. As our ship inched its way into the Upper Bay, night lifted and revealed the silhouettes of lower Manhattan in the distance. Just then, someone tapped me on the shoulder.

"We are all supposed to go below decks and stay out of sight," he said.

Four hours later, finally, we left the ship through a warehouse. We emerged out on the streets right in the middle of Manhattan. It was as abrupt a transition as one can imagine. A Greyhound bus was waiting, and soon we were on our way. Down the West Side Elevated Highway and through the Holland Tunnel; from there on through Philadelphia, Baltimore and on to Washington.

The trip south particularly impressed me: the large number of cars, even on Sunday; station wagons with wooden paneling; women's bright red topcoats; the long, long rows of Dutch style houses in Baltimore; the hamburger stand where we stopped for a quick bite; and the cosmopolitan appareance of Washington D.C., when we entered it after dark. Somewhere between Wash-ington and Alexandria we changed to an Army bus. Less than an hour later, we entered Fort Hunt, where we were to spend the next three weeks for screening.

We were the first group to be processed at this station. The earlier shipments had been screened at Fort Strong, near Boston. We were gradually allowed to move freely within certain areas of our confines, which included a foot walk to the Potomac River, through a short tunnel under the Mt. Vernon highway. The processing was done by Army Intelligence personnel, who all spoke flawless German.

The conduct and attitude of our escorts was correct and cooperative beyond reproach. As a result, our stay at Fort Hunt was very pleasant. I am sure that these favorable first impressions in those days have tided many of us over later periods of doubt. The first days were completely occupied with the filling out of forms, fingerprint taking, medical checks, and interviews. After that, it became relatively quiet. Besides reading, strolling, and an occasional movie in the evening, we devoted our time to learning English. One of the escorts had kindly agreed to hold informal classes. The barracks were immaculately clean and tidy, and were kept so by German prisoners of war. While there, rumors we had heard in Landshut, that we were headed for Fort Bliss, Texas, and White Sands, New Mexico, were confirmed.

We asked Carlson, one of the Army Intelligence men, what was going on down there, and what we would be doing. His answers were evasive. However, we had already deduced that the group had been subdivided into two sections: the smaller one stationed at White Sands Proving Grounds (now White Sands Missile Range), connected in some manner to intended launchings of V-2 missiles; and the larger, not too far away, at Fort Bliss, engaged in undisclosed studies. Information was scanty, yet sufficient enough to cast some doubt on the possibility that we would be finished within six months, the duration of our contract. It would not be done, if things continued at the pace of recent months.

It was at Fort Hunt that we received the sad news that Hans Lindenberg had unexpectedly passed away, the victim of an ailment which had been neglected during the war years and had suddenly caught up with him. He was buried at Fort Bliss.

On the evening of Thursday, February 21, we boarded a train

in Alexandria, to carry us south. The countryside was wintry; patches of snow were visible here and there. But, gradually, the scenery changed; the first palms came into view. During the most beautiful weather, we entered New Orleans. We remained close to the windows to catch all the sights. By late afternoon, our special car had been hitched to a train going west. We crossed the Mississippi River in a spectacular thunderstorm; then night fell. When the sun rose again, we were in Texas. Another 24 hours later, El Paso!

At Fort Bliss, we found ourselves surrounded by unfamiliar looking two-story wooden barracks, lined up along a road, several rows deep. We had stopped at one of these. Several other, lower buildings were nearby . . . and familiar faces! Welcomes were warm and boisterous. Soon, others emerged from the buildings, among them Wernher von Braun.

Later we "greenhorns" were shown around by the "old timers," as they humorously referred to themselves. Three of the two-story buildings had been set aside for the German group. There were three or four single story buildings: a messhall, an office building, and supply buildings. In a grove of cottonwood trees was a small house which had been converted by the German group members into a modest club house, where many of us used to gather in the evening, to play cards, make small purchases in a PX room, and have a beer or two.

Movement without escort was restricted, upon word of honor, to the immediate area of approximately six acres. There were no fences. Once every month, in groups of four, and with a soldier escort, each of us was permitted to go into El Paso to make purchases, to have a meal in one of the better restaurants, or just to stroll through the streets.

The messhall was operated by a group of German prisoners of war, simple, average people who were happy to have escaped the more serious consequences of the war, and who, with nothing else to do, devoted themselves with enthusiasm to their tasks. As a result, the food was excellent.

I spent my first evening in the club house, becoming familiar with fruit, vegetable, and real cocktails, and with the taste of American beer, which I found to be excellent. Sitting on couches and hammocks, "newcomers" and "old timers" soon were once again exchanging experiences and news. Next morning, I was impressed by the crisp cold, which contrasted sharply with the balmy air of the day before. El Paso is at an altitude of over 4,000 feet which explains the drastic diurnal temperature changes.

Two days later, a small group, among them von Braun and myself, left for White Sands by bus. In those days, it was not possible to drive directly across the desert. Rather, it was necessary to go around the Franklin Mountains, through El Paso, and on along the Rio Grande River to Las Cruces. From there, a spectacular ride brought us over the San Andres Pass, into the Tularosa Basin, where the proving grounds are located. Then and there, I fell in love with the countryside. To this day, although I have since explored nearly every corner of it, I never tire of these colorful, vast, open spaces, called the Southwest.

The small group at the White Sands Proving Grounds was housed in one-story barracks, which provided noticeably less space than we enjoyed at Fort Bliss. The twelve-to-fifteen people there were engaged in preparations for assembly of a number of V-2 rockets from a moderate selection of parts, brought to the U.S. from Germany before Russian occupation forces took over central Germany. These fifteen German specialists were assisted by a group of representatives from the General Electric Company and by a technical Army unit.

Facilities at White Sands in those days were nothing compared to what they are today. Only one modest hangar was available; a second one under construction. The assembly of the rocket parts, many of them extremely delicate, posed problems. Adequate laboratory facilities were absent, doubly felt in an area where sandstorms are frequent and temperature differentials between night and day might easily amount to 50 degrees Fahrenheit.

The entire program of bringing German specialists to this country has since become known as "Operation Paperclip," for reasons unknown to the author. Those affected, consequently, were called "Paperclip Specialists," a term frequently misunderstood, particularly in Germany, where translation was even less flattering. Until the files are opened, it will remain unknown what detailed plans had been made for this group during its first years in the United

States. Contractually, provisions were absolutely fair and just. The duration of the first contract period was six months, from signature date in Germany. During this period, the employees were to "undertake such research, design, development, and other tasks associated with jet propulsion and guided missiles, as may be assigned by competent U.S. authorities."

The contract, five typewritten pages long, contained many provisions covering such areas as: transportation to the U.S.; baggage allowance; religious activity; quarters and subsistence; dependents; termination; and numerous others. One particularly important and most valuable clause was that dependents, if they wished, could remain in the Landshut housing project. Especially important: if local German authorities were unable to provide food amounting to at least 2300 calories per day per person, U.S. authorities would augment this diet, cost to be borne by the employee.

Considering the fact that fighting on the European front had ceased less than a year before, the conditions of employment were considered to be fair and generous by all, even if interpretation by local administration may at times have been narrower.

There have been reports that the treatment of the German specialists was not fair, in some cases even hinting at better treatment afforded by the Russians. Nothing could be further from the truth. Of course, there were occasional gripes, by individuals or by the group. However, these were always about a specific item, but never about a basically and generally unsatisfactory situation.

Our contract provided: *"Restraint:* The group will not be under physical restraint, but must agree to remain in the area selected by the employer unless specific authority is granted to leave the area." This paragraph correctly sums up the actual situation, which confined us by request rather than by fence to an area which was initially small, but which gradually increased in size, until ultimately, upon issuance of "first papers," all restrictions had disappeared. It is probably noteworthy that during a period of almost four years, nothing of real significance happened that made the designers of the contract regret this generous and flexible contractual provision.

For several years, we spent our time with various studies, layouts, design, and some model test work for a project not concerning liquid propellant rocket systems. For approximately one year, we were stationed in the double decker barracks, where most of the study work was conducted. An empty hangar in a former automotive repair area became additionally available later. There was ample time for reading. We frequently visited a nearby Fort Bliss motion picture theatre. Besides being a diversion and entertainment, the movies afforded excellent opportunity to familiarize ourselves with the language.

We could also visit the post bowling alley. We formed teams, under the guidance of the "old timers" familiar with the American bowling rules, which differ markedly from the German ones, particularly as to scoring.

I particularly enjoyed several weekend Greyhound bus rides, which were arranged to historical places in the little towns along the Rio Grande; to the Ruidoso resort area in the mountains near Alamogordo; to a tennis match, Tilden against Perry; to an acquatic show. These occasions were immensely welcome, since, during the first year, contact with the outside world, in general, was rather limited.

A substantial portion of the group's spare time and per diem allowance went into the preparation of food parcels. Through common purchasing actions, large quantities of flour, sugar, lard, raisins, oats, and the like; of cartons, wrapping paper, strings, tape, and labels were purchased and distributed. Amounts were collected; parcels were packed, sealed, weighed, and delivered to the post office. These shipments were a great help to relatives and close friends in Germany, and helped to reduce many a desperate situation in these first years immediately after the war.

As one can imagine, confinement of over one hundred professional people in so small an area created problems from time to time. Some were matters which appeared to be very important and were taken very seriously at the time, spilling all the way up to, and engulfing the U.S.-German sponsored administration. Others sound somewhat amusing now, looking back over the years.

There was the case of one group member, who had developed the habit of going to the washroom, stark naked, save for a pair of wooden sandals, to the annoyance of many of his co-tenants, both esthetically, and acoustically. One day, unknown vigilantes nailed his wooden sandals to the floor with six-inch spikes, the protruding points of which they bent over in the ceiling below!

The general financial arrangements for the first two contractual terms of six months each were simple: a salary, in German currency and subject to German taxes, was paid to the dependents in Germany. It was subject to the general regulations, i.e., it could not be transferred out of Germany. The average yearly amount was approximately the currency-equivalent of $2500, but the purchasing power in Germany immediately after the war was much less. Since expenditures in the Landshut Camp were very small, most families deposited the amounts received in a savings bank. The men in America received a per diem of $6.00, from which $1.20 for housing was withheld. With the exception of the latter, this was considered quite satisfactory by all concerned. An interesting financial oddity occurred later, however. "Someone in Washington" found that U.S. taxes should also have been paid for the equivalent dollar value of the German salary as well as for that portion of the per diem which had not been used for housing or meals. Naturally, as good future U.S. citizens, we objected to the double taxation; a legal battle, with attorneys' fees, ensued. By the time the final decision was handed down that we had to pay the tax (plus 6% interest per year), the currency reform had become effective in Germany, reducing all monetary values to 5% of their original rate. Thus, the taxes paid turned out to be higher than the amounts received.

The per diem payments were made monthly, almost always consisting of one $100 bill and some smaller ones. Thus, one-hundred-dollar bills to us were a most common sight and we could not understand the excitement which resulted every time we had to "break" one in a local store or restaurant. The honorable citizens of El Paso probably gained the impression that a group of rich people was working "up there" at Fort Bliss.

It is probably interesting to mention that the nature of our group, our backgrounds and conditions of employment were little known, even in El Paso. An incident on a business trip to Rock Island Arsenal, Illinois, was typical. When our small group had a haircut, the barber in Molines soon noticed our peculiar English.

"Where are you fellows from?" he inquired.

"From Texas," we answered, almost in unison.

"Oh, I see." There were no further questions.

Only gradually, the Army released information about us DASE (Department of the Army Special Employees). On November 13, 1946, the El Paso *Herald Post* announced, "German Scientists To Be Interviewed. German Scientists of whom Fort Bliss officials speak in whispers, will answer questions for newspaper reporters soon."

The major press release occurred on December 4, 1946. Interviews followed. The reaction in most instances was very objective.

"118 Top German V-2 Experts Stationed in E. P.—Builders of Nazi Secret Weapons Working for U.S." wrote the El Paso *Times* on December 4, 1946.

A Washington release on the same day confirmed the news in an apparent answer to charges that "this country has let Russia and Great Britain skim off the cream of Germany's scientific brains and experience."

At the time of these releases, the group had just been moved into a new area, the war-time annex of the William Beaumont General Hospital. Gradual evacuation of the wards had made available considerably more space, making possible the setup of offices and a clearer subdivision of the working groups. The newspaper interviews were held on these premises, pictures of living quarters were taken, and human interest stories collected. The subsequent reports were very objective and cooperative. I recall one item, however, which stirred up considerable discussion. One of the German specialists had been conversing with a reporter about food. In faltering English, he had been expressing his preference for stewed chicken over well-broiled. Groping for words, he used the term "rubberizing" in reference to broiling. He found himself most embarrassed the next day by a newspaper headline, "German Scientist Says American Cooking Tasteless; Dislikes Rubberized Chicken"; and by an irate German group trying to divorce themselves from such statements by means of a long list of signatures.

Yet, life went on.

"German Scientists Plan Re-fueling Station in Sky on Route to

Moon," read a headline of the El Paso *Herald Post* in December 1946, describing a "space platform."

"Jobs for German Scientists Opposed," then read a newspaper story on March 27, 1947, referring to a statement by the Federation of American Scientists, who considered the "wholesale importation of scientists as not in keeping with the best objectives of American and foreign policy" and as "an affront to the people of all countries who so recently fought beside us."

"They'll do us less damage here," expressed an editorial the next day, requesting that the FAS "first amend their protest to declare that Russia's importation of hundreds of German scientists to work in Soviet laboratories was an affront to the American people."

"German Scientists in El Paso Blasted," announced an El Paso *Times* headline on July 1, 1947, referring to a House address by Democratic Representative John Dingell, who felt that he "had never thought that we were so poor mentally . . . to have to import for the defense of our country." He also felt that "Germans were so far behind . . . that they were looking for radium as if it was a substance for toothpaste; they must have confused it with Bob Hope's irium."

The retort followed promptly:

"General Denies Army Has Feted Bliss Germans," was the headline of the El Paso *Herald Post,* continuing, " 'German Scientists at Ft. Bliss are doing wonderful work,' says Congressman Thomason."

Gradually, the controversy subsided and headlines began to read,

"German Pupils Sing 'Eyes of Texas'—Like to Recite Pledge to U.S. Flag" (El Paso *Herald Post,* August 5, 1947).

"Speak English Contests Help Americanize Children of Germans" wrote the *Herald Post* a few weeks later.

Years later (July 11, 1954), the Chattanooga *Times* settled the matter once and for all with the headline:

"German Scientists Bring Knowledge and Pumpernickel to Huntsville."

During 1946, following the arrival of my own shipment, the number of German specialists in the Fort Bliss/White Sands Group gradually increased further to a total of approximately 130. At irregular intervals, individuals arrived, who had been detained, some to finish a degree, others to take care of urgent personal affairs, or those who, as in a few cases, had not immediately been located in the post-war mixup. One of the groups which joined us in the summer of 1946 was a company of about half a dozen men who had arrived in the States with one of the early shipments, but who had been detached to the Aberdeen Proving Grounds in Maryland, to classify, sift, and catalogue the Peenemünde secret files, the very same files I had helped to hide in that mine in central Germany. All of the material was subsequently made available to the United States' allies and to American industry.

During the period from 1947 through the early 1950's, very few additional men arrived from Germany. After the later activation of the Army Ballistic Missile Agency at Redstone Arsenal, Huntsville, Alabama, in the early 1950's, recruiting trips to Germany were initiated, but the results were very meager. In the vigorous revitalization of German industry, almost all former rocket specialists had grown into good positions and declined the offer of the U.S. Government and certain private parties. A limited number of engineering talent, however, did come to the U.S. during the later years.

One of the difficulties with which the cognizant U.S. authorities found themselves confronted for several years was the fact that the German group had been brought to this country under special laws, rather than through regular immigration procedures. During these years, therefore, we did not have regular identification papers. It also explains why the freedom of movement was increased only cautiously. Retrospectively, a certain reluctance to loosen up may seem to have been overcautious. It appears to be understandable, however, if one considers that only a few miles separated us from the Mexican border.

Our first ID cards had read:

THIS CARD IS NOT A SPECIAL AUTHORIZATION

The bearer of this card, whose photograph and signature appear hereon, is hereby authorized to be present on such military reservations as may be designated on the reverse side. He is not authorized in restricted areas, except as specifically designated. In the event that this card is presented off a military reservation to civilian authorities, including state, federal and municipal police, without verification by *military personnel* of *this office* and *supporting papers,* it is requested that this office be notified immediately and that the authorities concerned assure themselves that the bearer of this card is placed in transport of this office. (Phone or telegraph . . . Res & Dev Div Sub-O (Rkt) Fort Bliss, Texas, Extension 4235). Inasmuch as the bearer of this card is a SPECIAL WAR DEPARTMENT EMPLOYEE, he will *NOT* be interrogated, or asked for further proof of identity, without permission from this office.

Then, on September 9, 1946, in a *Hauptversammlung,* it was announced, and received with great elation, that a letter had arrived from Washington, saying that all restrictions of movement had been dropped. New passes would be issued shortly. Four days later, in correction of a previous misunderstanding or due to someone's cold feet, the announcement was drastically reduced to include only the area of greater El Paso. Passes were issued accordingly. Like many others, I did not feel particularly disappointed. This new freedom was so much more than our six acre confinement that I thoroughly enjoyed it.

The move into the new area, commonly simply referred to as the "Annex," took place on October 23, 1946. This was another substantial improvement of our daily routine. Each member now had a relatively quiet room of his own. My own window faced north, overlooking the nearby highway along the Biggsfield Air Field. There was constant traffic, life, and visible contact with the outside world.

Our move into the Annex was almost coincident with the publication of the first drafts of a new contract, which extended the employment periods to yearly intervals, provided for the shipment of the immediate families, and changed the payments entirely to U.S. currency, with the per diem discontinued. There were numerous other provisions of routine nature. By November 22, 1946, the contracts were distributed for signature. As with the original contracts, provisions were entirely fair and for the first time contained the necessary legal groundwork for later benefits, notably the assurance that efforts would be made to clear the way for obtaining a regular visa "provided the personal conduct and political background of the contractor justifies this." Exaggerated salary figures have occasionally been quoted for this period. The fact is that the average amount was less than $450 per month, with the very highest figure in the group, which included W. von Braun, at $675 per month. These figures remained unchanged for three years.

U.S. authorities fulfilled one of their principal obligations with extreme promptness. On December 8, 1946, the first few families arrived, followed by others at intervals. On May 23, 1947, Irmel arrived in New York, and four days later, we were united again. The average time of separation of the families had been slightly over one year.

For a few months, these families had to put up in former hospital wards and other quarters not originally intended as apartments. However, conversion of a selected number of these wards into four-apartment units was already in progress at that time. When the conversion work started, we wondered what possibly could be made out of these temporary buildings. But, as the subdivisions and interiors gradually took shape, the apartments turned out to be much nicer than the exterior of the wards would have suggested.

During most of 1947, we were permitted to make trips, even distant ones, during our vacations. A few of the group members, by this time, had purchased used cars, among them Magnus von Braun. Shortly after Irmel had arrived, a small group, which included Irmel and myself, took off with Magnus for a trip to the Grand Canyon, the Sierra Nevada, the Utah parks, and California. As one can imagine, the impact of this experience left a lasting impression on all of us.

During 1948, the restrictions were temporarily tightened again, initially to El Paso and the Fort Bliss military reservation, which is a very large, but rather unexciting area; then to the area within a radius of 200 miles around Fort Bliss. Half of this circle, naturally, fell "south of the border"; the other half, of course, did not amount to as much as it would have in, for instance, New York.

In the summer of 1948, when I was in charge of an altitude test facility, our equipment was transferred into the high mountains near Bishop, California, for approximately four months. A few months after my return from this assignment, our boy Frank was born. He turned out to be a very special person. Not only was he a genuine Texan, but he was also the first U.S. citizen in the family, born to parents who legally were not even there. His birth-date, preceding Irmel's and my legal entry date by almost two years, subsequently confused many an official.

Another addition to the family at that time was an old prewar Studebaker Champion, which, prior to its final collapse, took us to many beautiful spots in the Southwest, and up into Colorado. It also carried me on a brief trip to Los Angeles. Enroute to the West Coast, I ran into a road block near Lordsburg, N.M., set up to look for wetbacks who might have crossed the nearby border. A long row of cars was waiting in front of me. Eventually, the controlling trooper arrived at my car. Politely he inquired:

"U.S. citizen?"

"No."

"Your place of birth?"

"Essen, Germany."

"Place of legal entry?"

"Sorry, no legal entry."

The officer looked baffled for a moment, then assumed a professional, alert attitude, with a quick side glance to his colleague checking the row of cars headed in the opposite direction.

"How did you get here?"

"I came from El Paso, on my way to Los Angeles."

"I mean, how did you come to this country?"

"I was brought here by the Army as a special employee."

"Never heard of it; you have any papers?"

"Yes, right here."

I handed him my simple typewritten authorization which read:

HEADQUARTERS

RESEARCH & DEVELOPMENT SERVICE SUBOFFICE
(ROCKET)

FORT BLISS, TEXAS

RECREATIONAL LEAVE AUTHORIZATION

Dieter Huzel

The above named War Department Special Employee is authorized to leave the limits of Fort Bliss, Texas during off duty hours for the purpose of recreational trips.

In event of an accident or injury, please notify this headquarters by telephoning Main 2404, Extension 8-2211.

By ORDER OF MAJOR HAMILL:

> GORDON A. McGANNON
> 1st Lt., Ord. Dept.
> Adjutant

As he was reading, his facial expression relaxed. Smiling he said,

"Now I remember. I did hear about you fellows. Hadn't run into one yet, though. Well, good luck."

Relieved, I was on my way again.

In early 1950, the first concrete steps were taken to initiate legal status for the group members. Extensive form filling ensued; then the legal entry followed. For this purpose, we were all brought across the border, to the U.S. consulate in Ciudad Juarez, Mexico. Following processing of our forms and issuance of visas, we returned, this time processed in a routine fashion at the border. Because of the proximity of the two cities, Juarez and El Paso, the entire procedure took no more than a few hours; even left time for a first, excellent Mexican meal in a small border restaurant.

For some time it had been rumored that we would be moved to Redstone Arsenal at Huntsville, Alabama. These rumors were now confirmed officially. In a way, this was a formal recognition, at last, by the U.S. Government of the significance of rocketry, for the move heralded the availability of far superior facilities and vastly larger budgets. And it signaled recognition by America in general that we were no longer "War Department Special Employees," no longer "super-engineers" secreted in a mysterious desert development center, but human beings free to come and go as we wished and to pursue our chosen profession.

For me personally, it raised problems. I had been suffering

from allergies and hayfever in Germany. This condition had been confined, however, to brief periods in the summer. Here in El Paso my troubles now lasted practically all year long. From all indications, the climatic conditions in Alabama did not appear any more favorable. And then, of course, the prospect of having to leave the Southwest did not appeal to me, either. Although it meant leaving a group in which I had so many good friends, with whom I had been associated for years, and so many capable and brilliant associates and teachers, Wernher von Braun in particular, I decided to remain in the West. With the understanding blessing of then Colonel H. N. Toftoy, I obtained permission to apply for a job in the Aerophysics Laboratory (now Rocketdyne Division), of North American Aviation in Los Angeles, a leading company in the field of liquid propellant rocket engines.

After my application had been accepted, we moved to Los Angeles in June, 1950. Less than a year later, our daughter Renata was born, bringing the number of U.S. citizens in the family to two, a Texan and a Californian, with the parents still having four years to go toward their naturalization.

When I joined the Aerophysics Laboratory, it was a comparatively small division of North American Aviation. The company, at that time, was in the earlier phases of the development of powerplants for a long range missile program. During the second half of 1950, while I was concentrating on familiarizing myself with my new job and with the new experience of living outside of a regulated housing project, the move of the Fort Bliss group to Huntsville was completed. Shortly afterward, it was assigned the development of the Army's Redstone missile.

When the Redstone group had completed their surveys, layouts, and preliminary designs, it turned out that one of North American's intermediate phase rocket engines almost perfectly met the requirements of their missile. The modifications required to make a flyable engine system out of this development tool were accomplished smoothly and expeditiously, while the subsequent phases of North American's original project proceeded separately.

At about the time the new powerplant, modified for Redstone use, was subjected to its first static firing tests, I had the good fortune of being assigned as Development Engineer in charge of

this engine, now commonly referred to as the "Redstone Engine."
Thus quite unexpectedly, I was working closely again with many
of my former Fort Bliss associates.

By late March 1953, things had progressed to the point where
the first static firing tests of a complete missile could be scheduled
at Redstone Arsenal's own facilities, which at that time were in
their very first beginnings. With interruptions, I spent several
months at Huntsville, helping with the series of static firings, until
the first missile was considered ready for flight, and for transfer
to the Cape Canaveral launching site. During my stay at Huntsville,
I did not have to worry about what to do with my spare time.
Practically every evening I was a guest with the family of one or
another of von Braun's original group, exchanging experiences
during the past three years.

Early in August, the launching date for Redstone Missile No. 1
was set for August 20th. Three days ahead of that date, a small
group of North American representatives went to Florida. It included Sam Hoffman, our General Manager; Bill Cecka, Chief
of Test; Chan Hamlin, Redstone Project Engineer; Norm Reuel,
Engine Development Chief; Ed Prono, our valve specialist; Dave
Hatfield, Redstone field service representative; and myself.

It was my first trip to Florida. When we arrived at Melbourne
Beach, it was raining. With the rain, the August heat, and the lush
vegetation, a distinct "tropical" impression prevailed. We stayed
at the Tradewinds Hotel in nearby Indialantic, a venerable, quiet,
extremely relaxing spot, far away from the hustle-bustle of the
fashionable places, and from the base at Cape Canaveral, for that
matter.

We had dinner at one of the excellent restaurants in the area,
right on the beach. From the terrace, one could see the moonlit
crowns of the waves. The gentle sound of the pounding surf filled
the air. There was no mistake, the salty smell of the breeze was
"Atlantic." It was so much like Peenemünde, I thought, on one of
those rare hot summer evenings.

On the next day, the members of our North American group
familiarized themselves thoroughly with the Cape Canaveral
facilities and with the progress of launch preparations. The
launching crew was well on schedule, and preliminary checkout

tests had shown the powerplant to be in good shape. There was little for us to do but wait for the final checkout tests and the launch itself.

On August 19, we went to bed early. At midnight, Hatfield knocked at the doors of the immediate participants, Eddie Prono and myself. Drowsily, we crawled out of our beds. During the one hour drive to the Cape we had ample time to wake up completely.

There was a bustle of activity around the launching pad. Floodlights glared and brightly illuminated the missile which was painted with a black and white pattern. It was almost dwarfed by the giant Noble crane, which embraced it with its working platforms. Helmeted technicians and engineers were active on the three or four platforms, engaged in last checkouts and adjustments of the guidance system on the upper elevations and of the powerplant components at the lower decks. Two elevators were crawling up and down the sides of the structure. From time to time, announcements came over the PA system, often with a distinct Alabama drawl, sometimes with an unmistakable German accent. At regular intervals, a jeep with an insecticide nebulizer circled the pad, emitting dense, white, ill-smelling clouds, leaving us wondering who remained more affected, the abundant and aggressive mosquitoes or ourselves.

Despite many secondary differences, the similarity of the Cape Canaveral atmosphere to that of the Peenemünde days was striking. Many of the faces were the same: Dr. Kurt Debus, who during my days at P-7 had been chief of the guidance team, and who was now in charge of the entire Redstone launch operation; Albert Zeiler, Chief Redstone Powerplant Engineer, just as he had been so many times during V-2 launchings; and a number of others. The reeds in the background, the ocean behind them, and the salt air; the technical matters, the checkouts, the fueling procedures, and the familiar tension as the hour advanced; but above all, the simple fact that we were about to launch a large rocket.

I did not know it then, but a missile exactly like the one we were preparing was to carry the first American satellite into space, and later, America's first astronaut. Yet, even if we didn't know this, we all felt the significance of our undertaking, of its far reaching implications. *This* is what made the atmosphere so much like Peenemünde. I am sure we would have felt just the same if we had been at the White Sands Missile Range, with no ocean, no sea breeze within hundreds of miles, or later at Vandenberg Air Force Base, on the rocky shores of the Pacific.

Launch time had been set at 7 a.m., E.S.T. There were a few delays, however. The Base Radio Plane, which was to warn ships to stay out of the trajectory area, had mechanical trouble; then a tracking radar beacon conked out; then a ship had been sighted in the target area. Oh, so typical, so normal, so familiar!

The missile took off at 9:35 a.m., E.S.T., and "Redstone No. 1," the first big American missile, was on its way. I could not see it for more than a few seconds from my observation window in the control center. When, at long last, we were permitted to leave the shelter, all that remained was a quiet summer morning in Florida, under an overcast sky. There was no trace or reminder of the historical event that had taken place a few minutes ago. Soon, outside observers arrived from more distant stations and excitedly reported how they had followed the rocket while it was accelerating to faster and faster speeds, until it disappeared abruptly in the clouds. Even though telemetering records soon revealed that, owing to a guidance malfunction, the missile had not traveled its full distance, we were all overjoyed and excited.

The ring was closed. It had started in Peenemünde and was now continuing at Cape Canaveral. When later generations look back on this period, they will see the two events, the two locations, as one, just as a distant double star appears as a single light. Indeed, leaving Peenemünde was not the end of a road but, in truth, the beginning of the long, long road to the stars.

APPENDIX A

Rocketry in Germany

Historical Notes

Peenemünde and the V-2 were neither a beginning nor an end, certainly, in the new engineering science of the large rocket engine. One might say they represented the end of its adolescent period. Properly, the beginning of rocketry as a practical engineering effort must be given as 1919. In that year America's Professor Robert H. Goddard published his now-famous treatise, *A Method of Reaching Extreme Altitudes*. This document contained the germ of the modern science of rocketry. But it elicited little response in the country of its origin, and America missed its chance to lead the way. It remained for a man named Oberth to fire the imagination of his German compatriots.

1923

Hermann Oberth, a German professor from Mediasch, Rumania, published *The Rocket to Outer Space*. In this volume, the concept of the liquid propellant rocket was advanced, and the idea fell on fertile soil.

1927

On July 5, the *Verein fuer Raumschiffahrt*, the famous *VfR*, "Society for Space Travel," was founded by Johann Winkler in Breslau, Germany. In its initial membership were such men as Klaus Riedel, Rudolf Nebel, and Max Valier.

231

1928

On March 12, Kurt Volkhart drove the first rocket car, powered by solid propellants, at Ruesselsheim, Germany. Max Valier and F. Sander designed the car, which was built under the sponsorship of Fritz von Opel. Meanwhile, there was another sign of awakening popular interest in the rocket: Fritz Lang produced the film *Frau im Mond*, "The Girl in the Moon," for Ufa in Berlin—with Hermann Oberth acting as technical advisor.

1929

Hermann Oberth published *Means to Space Travel*.

1930

The *VfR* acquired part of an old military training field in Berlin-Reinickendorf for rocket testing. They named this "Rocket Air Field," but because of lack of funds their testing was severely limited. During the year, Wernher von Braun joined the *VfR;* and Dr. Walter Dornberger, then a captain, established an unofficial Army relationship with the *VfR* at Reinickendorf. He effected a contribution of 5,000 marks—about $1,200—from Col. Karl Becker to bolster the *VfR*'s sagging test activity.

1932

The cognizant Army Ordnance department, *Wa Pruef 1/1,* under Becker, renewed its interest in liquid propellant rockets. Wernher von Braun was hired and assigned to Dornberger, who had already been active in the solid propellant field for some time. On November 1, Army Ordnance activated "Test Station West" at Kummersdorf, twenty miles south of Berlin. The staff included von Braun, Klaus Riedel, and Arthur Rudolph.

1933

On January 30, Hitler came to power in Germany. During the year, the *VfR* dissolved itself, the result of a long-drawn-out internal conflict.

1934

In December, two A-2 rockets developed at Kummersdorf, were

launched from the North Sea island of Borkum. These were fairly successful launchings; the rockets developed approximately 2,200 pounds of thrust and achieved about one-and-one-half miles altitude.

1936

Army General von Fritsch witnessed a static firing of an A-3 at Kummersdorf, and was sufficiently impressed to lend his support to the rocket program. In April, Air Force General Kesselring and Army Col. Becker made a decision to build a joint Army-Air Force rocket development center. The northern tip of Usedom Island was selected as the site: the mouth of the Peene River, Peenemünde. As a part of this development, Dornberger's section was made into a separate department, *Wa Pruef 11,* "Department for Special Ordnance Devices." At this time the first A-4—V-2—concepts began to take shape. In August, ground was broken at the Peenemünde site.

1937

The majority of the Kummersdorf crew, which had grown from eight in 1932 to approximately one hundred, was transferred to Peenemünde. Peenemünde was divided into an Air Force Area (*Werk West:* V-1, He 176, Me 163, and other development efforts), and an Army Ordnance Area (*Werk Ost* and *Werk Süd:* A-4, *Wasserfall, Taifun,* and other developments). On August 18, a new German "Society for Space Research," *Gesselschaft fuer Weltraumforschung,* was founded by H. K. Kaiser in Berlin. Its activity remained limited, however. The first A-5 launchings, meanwhile, were made from the "Greifswalder Oie" Island, near Usedom.

1938

On April 18, the first A-4 static firing was conducted, on Test Stand P-1.

1939

In September, Hitler invaded Poland and World War II began.

1940

During the summer, the remainder of the Kummersdorf personnel were transferred to Peenemünde. This group included Dr. Walter Thiel. In August, static firings of the A-4 were begun on Stand P-7.

1941

On June 22, Hitler invaded Russia.

1942

On June 13, the first A-4 launching attempt was made. It was only partially successful. On October 3, the first successful launching of an A-4 was conducted.

1943

On August 17-18, RAF "Operation Crossbow" was carried out: The first air raid on Peenemünde. In December, mass production of the A-4 missile was begun in the subterranean plant *Mittelwerke,* near Nordhausen in central Germany.

1944

During the summer, three more raids were launched against Peenemünde; these were daylight raids (July 18, August 4, and August 25).

1945

During January and February, Peenemünde was evacuated. In March, the Peenemünde site was occupied by the Russian army. In April, the Americans occupied *Mittelwerke.* In May, the majority of the Peenemünde employees were taken into American custody in southern Bavaria.

APPENDIX B

German Rockets of the "A" Series

The A-4, known to the world as the V-2, was by no means the final stage in German rocket thinking. Including the A-4's progenitors, no less than eleven different rocket configurations were either tested or had passed into the design stage by the time Peenemünde ceased to exist as a German rocket facility.

A-1

This, the grandfather of most modern rockets, was developed at Kummersdorf. It incorporated a pressure-fed propellant system, utilized liquid oxygen and 75% alcohol, and generated 660 pounds of thrust for a duration of 16 seconds. Takeoff weight was 330 pounds; it was four and one-half feet long, one foot in diameter, and was stabilized by a 90-pound gyroscope in its tip. It was never launched; subsequent studies indicated that it was nose-heavy. The first attempt at a static firing was made December 21, 1932. Result: Explosion.

A-2

This rocket was similar to the A-1, but with the gyroscope located in the center of the rocket in an attempt to get away from the nose-heavy condition. The first two A-2's were launched in December, 1934 from the North Sea island of Borkum.

A-3

This was the first Peenemünde design. It also incorporated a pressure-fed propellant system, and utilized liquid oxygen and

75% alcohol. The A-3 generated 3,300 pounds of thrust for a duration of 45 seconds. Weight at takeoff was 1,650 pounds; the missile was 25 feet long, and two and one-half feet in diameter. For guidance, a three-gyroscope system and tungsten alloy jet vanes were used; the latter were of course inactive after engine cutoff. The velocity of the A-3 at engine cutoff was subsonic. Several were launched, with a maximum of 7.5 miles altitude and 11 miles range being attained.

A-4

This, of course, was the V-2, and it was beyond all comparison the principal development item at Peenemünde. Instead of pressure-fed propellants, a turbopump was incorporated; liquid oxygen and 75% alcohol were still the main propellants. The turbopump was powered by an 80% hydrogen peroxide steam generator. At sea level, the A-4 developed 56,000 pounds of thrust for 65 seconds duration. Its weight at takeoff was 28,500 pounds; it was 46.2 feet in length and 5.4 feet in diameter. Its nominal range was 200 miles, although some special versions were built which reached up to 250 miles. At engine cutoff, the A-4's velocity was 3,600 miles per hour; the apex of its trajectory was at an altitude of 60 miles. Impact velocity was 1,750 miles per hour. It delivered a 2,200-pound payload. The A-4 was a true ballistic missile.

A-5

This was actually an improved A-3, designed primarily as a test vehicle for A-4 guidance equipment, and preceded the latter in time. It had the same dimensions as the A-3, and included graphite jet steering vanes and a parachute recovery device. Approximately eighty A-5's were launched, including some refurbished after a previous launching.

A-6

This was to have been a subsonic missile. It never passed beyond the preliminary analysis stage.

A-7

The A-7 was planned as a research tool for the contemplated

A-9. It was essentially a winged A-5, and it was conceived in two models. One, a "replica" without a propulsion system, to be dropped from a plane at an altitude of 26,000 feet, with a range of some 28 miles expected. In the Fall of 1942, two drops were attempted; both were unsuccessful. The second model was to have included a propulsion system delivering about 4,000 pounds of thrust, and was to have a 16-mile range. It was never built.

A-8

This was a projected development of the A-4 to the 66,000-pound thrust, 90-second-duration level. Nitric acid and kerosene were to be used as the main propellants. No A-8's were built.

A-9

This was to be the second-stage rocket for use with the A-10 booster; this combination was the final goal of the "A" series of rocket development. The A-9 was essentially a winged A-4; launched without the booster, it was to have a 500-mile range. Air vanes were incorporated which would be active during the entire flight time. The A-9 was to have delivered a 2,200-pound payload, but the missile concept never passed beyond the preliminary analysis stage.

A-10

This was the projected booster for the A-9, and the combination represents the first intercontinental ballistic missile design— a 2,600-mile range was expected. The A-10 was to produce 440,000 pounds of thrust for 50 seconds. The takeoff weight of the A-9/A-10 combination would have been 192,000 pounds, the propellant load alone representing 136,000 pounds of this. The length of the A-9/A-10 combination was 72 feet; diameter was 12 feet. Like the A-9, the A-10 remained on the drawing boards.

A-4b

This planned modification of the A-4 was prompted by the loss of seashore launching bases in Holland. It was a winged A-4 with the A-9 aft section. In late 1944, two preliminary models, still with the A-4 aft section, were launched vertically, to enable a study of wing behavior in the sonic and supersonic region. About 1,460 miles per hour (approximately Mach 2) was achieved. At war's end, five more were in the buildup state.

Test Facilities at Peenemünde

Much of this story of Peenemünde's last days centered around Stand P-7. This was certainly the major A-4 test complex at the plant; but there were actually twelve distinct test facilities at Peenemünde, plus a thirteenth which never passed out of the design stage.

P-1

This was a vertical stand for static firing of the complete A-4 missile. It was equipped with a water-cooled tubular-wall flame deflector (i.e., the structure of the deflector consisted essentially of tubes through which the cooling water was forced under high pressure). No gimbaling system for attitude testing was provided on this stand. P-1 could accommodate thrusts up to 100 tons.

P-2

This was a model-engine test stand, the first ever built for engines in which nitric acid was employed as one of the propellants. Thrust accommodation was ten tons.

P-3

This stand was used for research investigations with bipropellant gas generators and turbines, as well as for injection systems.

P-4

Originally an assisted-take-off firing stand, this was later converted to the *Meiller-Wagen* shop.

P-5

Used for hydrogen peroxide steam generator system development and calibration, and for heat exchanger development. Initially, this stand was also used for A-4 engine cold calibrations.

P-6

Originally a static-firing stand for A-5 combustion chambers, but later converted for testing *Wasserfall* chambers. Burst-diaphragm tests were also conducted at P-6.

P-7

The principal A-4 test facility. It included an assembly hangar with six booths for complete rocket checkout (later enlarged by the addition of balconies); three movable static-firing structures operating with one double-sided water-cooled tubular-wall flame deflector (permitting gimbaling of the entire A-4 missile in two planes); two launching pads; and one cold-calibration pad for engines only. Both static firings and launchings were conducted from P-7. Static-firing thrust accommodation: Up to 200 tons.

P-8

An A-4 combustion chamber static-firing and calibration stand. The system was pressurized, and tests for the full design duration of the components could be performed. Although the main valves were manually operated (!), a highly trained crew could put two chambers per hour through their paces on P-8.

P-9

A dual test stand for static-firing of *Wasserfall* combustion chambers and complete *Wasserfall* rockets.

P-10

Adjacent to P-7, and operated as a part of P-7, this was a separate launching pad with its own control center. This was the test launching site for motorized A-4 units (i.e., V-2 batteries).

P-11

This was to have been the A-4 production missile test stand, where static firings for calibration and quality control of the *Mittelwerke* product were to be conducted. Its capacity was one complete rocket test per day. The intention was that ten percent of the production missiles were to be fired by this and two never-finished identical adjacent stands. Actually, only forty firings were ever conducted on P-11 during its short life. Activated in June, 1943, it was destroyed in the air raid of July 18, 1944. Its equipment included four preparation stands with provision for performing cold calibrations, suspension for gimbaling tests, and a one-sided tubular-wall water-cooled flame deflector.

P-12

This was the code name for a proposed submarine-towed A-4 launching facility, but it never passed beyond the preliminary design stage. Some hardware had been built by the war's end: An experimental towed vehicle, some loading gear, and a replica of a flame deflector.

Schwimmweste

This means "life-belt" and it was the code name for a floating static-firing stand, moored in Peenemünde harbor. It was used for a few *Wasserfall* tests.

INDEX

243